The Great Controversy

between good & evil

Bible Study Guide

Revelation Publications

- Compatible with any Bible
- Individuals or groups
- Contains full answer key!

The commentary following the questions is the original text adapted from 13 of the last 14 chapters of ***The Great Controversy*** by E.G.White. In an effort to keep the study guide to a practical length some chapters have been shortened. To omit any text was a difficult task because this entire work is a rich blessing. The author highly recommends each Bible student acquire and read this wonderful book in its entirety. To obtain your personal copy contact the publisher for more information.

The Great Controversy Bible Study Guide

Revelation Publications
P.O. Box 700, Tontitown, AR 72770
www.RevelationPublications.com

Questions and compilation by Merlin Beerman
Editor - V.C. Darmody
Appendix by Merlin Beerman
Appendix Content Editors - Ron Ray and Scott Cassell
Illustrations - Copyright (C) Justinen Creative Group, Inc., Nampa ID
Cover Layout - Adam Dean

Commentary adapted from ***The Great Controversy*** by E.G.White

Printed in the U.S.A.

ISBN 0-9668482-5-X

TABLE OF CONTENTS

AN INVITATION TO THE READER

We arc glad you have received *The Great Controversy Bible Study Guide*. It is our prayer that you will go through these lessons and draw closer to Christ; the One who offers you friendship, peace, and eternal life.

If there is an address in the box below, this guide is offered to you as a gift from a Bible school. Your school may utilize this guide in one of two possible ways.

The guide may or may not contain an answer section in the back. When there is one, you may refer to it to verify your answers. Upon completion, if you wish to have your certificate validated, remove and send only your certificate to the address below for signature by an instructor.

If an address is present but your guide does not contain an answer section; then, upon completion, you may send your entire completed guide for verification and have your certificate signed.

In either situation, all you have mailed to us will be returned with additional free study materials. If at any time you have additional Bible questions, you may send them, and an instructor will respond.

You may have been a Christian all your life, or this may be your first opportunity to learn about the wonderful love of Jesus; in either case, this time you spend in the Word of God will be a rich blessing. May the Lord fill you with peace as you seek to know Him better.

FOR MORE STUDY MATERIALS WRITE:

SUGGESTIONS FOR INDIVIDUAL STUDY

(1) PRAY FOR GUIDANCE

Each time you study, pray for discernment and the guidance of the Holy Spirit. Approach your study with an open mind. Avoid preconceived ideas that may have a negative influence on your search for truth.

(2) READ THE QUESTION

Read each question slowly taking extra time to contemplate and understand it. This will result in the greatest benefit from your study.

(3) FIND THE ANSWER

Use any Bible to look up the reference text listed below the answer space. Read the reference and surrounding texts to gain an understanding of their context. Write a concise answer on the blanks provided in your study guide. If you want to confirm your answer you may look it up in the answer section located in the back.

For a deeper understanding, read and compare the reference texts in multiple versions of Scripture. Use a concordance, column references, and a dictionary to look up unfamiliar words and search for other related texts.

(4) CONTEMPLATE THE RESULTS

Reread the question and answer, then read the commentary. Contemplate the significance of what you have just studied and ask for wisdom from the Lord to help you know how to apply it to your life.

(5) CONTINUE TO STUDY

It is our prayer that you will continue to study God's Word. We encourage you to contact your source for this guide and obtain other inspirational materials that will aid in your spiritual growth.

SUGGESTIONS FOR GROUP STUDY

(1) ASSIGN A LEADER	It is important to appoint an individual to lead your study group. This may be a pastor, church leader, or a shared responsibility among the group members. This individual's responsibility is to keep the discussion objective and encourage participation.
(2) PREDETERMINE STUDY METHODS	Make a group decision whether to include outside materials in your study sessions. As a rule, study time will be most fruitful when the focus is on Biblical references.
(3) PRE-STUDY THE LESSON	Encourage each member of your group to study the lesson prior to meeting. This will result in the greatest benefit to each individual as well as enhancing his/her ability to participate in discussion.
(4) BEGIN WITH PRAYER	Each time you meet always invite the Lord to be present in your study session and the Holy Spirit to be your guide.
(5) READ QUESTION	The group leader may read or appoint another member of the group to read the questions.
(6) READ ANSWER & COMMENTARY	The group leader can ask for volunteers to give the answer and related commentary. When time allows, ask for answers derived from various translations to increase participation and understanding.
(7) DISCUSSION	The most benefit will be gained if the leader does not lecture the group but rather leads it. Each member of the group should be encouraged to participate in the capacity he/she is comfortable with. One member of the group should not dominate the discussion. Encourage sensitivity to the feelings and opinions of others even in disagreement.
(8) TESTIMONY	Have a time at the beginning or end of your session for brief testimonies. This can be general or limited to the subject matter being studied.

The Origin of Evil - 1

(1) WHY IS GOD NOT RESPONSIBLE FOR SIN?

___

___

___

James 1:13

It is impossible to explain the origin of sin so as to give a reason for its existence. Yet enough may be understood concerning both the origin and the final disposition of sin to make fully manifest the justice and benevolence of God in all His dealings with evil. Nothing is more plainly taught in Scripture than that God was in no wise responsible for the entrance of sin; that there was no arbitrary withdrawal of divine grace, no deficiency in the divine government, that gave occasion for the uprising of rebellion.

(2) WHAT IS THE BIBLICAL DEFINITION OF SIN?

___

___

___

1 John 3:4; 2 Thessalonians 2:7

Sin is an intruder, for whose presence no reason can be given. It is mysterious, unaccountable; to excuse it is to defend it. Could excuse for it be found, or cause be shown for its existence, it would cease to be sin. Our only definition of sin is that given in the word of God; it is "the transgression of the law;" it is the outworking of a principle at war with the great law of love which is the foundation of the divine government.

(3) WHAT FOUR FUNDAMENTAL PRINCIPLES CHARACTERIZE THE GOVERNMENT OF GOD?

____

____

____

Psalms 89:14

The law of love being the foundation of the government of God, the happiness of all created beings depended upon their perfect accord with its great principles of righteousness. God desires from all His creatures the service of love-homage that springs from an intelligent appreciation of His character. He takes no pleasure in a forced allegiance, and to all He grants freedom of will, that they may render Him voluntary service.

(4) WHO VIOLATED GOD'S LAW AND BECAME THE AUTHOR OF SIN?

____

____

____

Isaiah 14:12; Revelation 12:7-9

But there was one that chose to pervert this freedom. Sin originated with him who, next to Christ, had been most honored of God and who stood highest in power and glory among the inhabitants of heaven.

(5) IN WHAT STATE DID GOD CREATE LUCIFER?

____

____

Ezekiel 28:15

Before his fall, Lucifer was first of the covering cherubs, holy and undefiled.

(6) WHAT PHYSICAL TRAIT DID LUCIFER CHOOSE TO DWELL UPON WHICH EVENTUALLY BROUGHT HIM TO THE SINFUL DESIRE OF SELF-EXULTATION?

____

____

____

Ezekiel 28:17

Lucifer might have remained in favor with God, beloved and honored by all the angelic host, exercising his noblc powers to bless others and to glorify his Maker. . . . Little by little, Lucifer came to indulge a desire for self-exaltation. . . . Instead of seeking to make God supreme in the affections and allegiance of His creatures, it was Lucifer's endeavor to win their service and homage to himself. And coveting the honor which the infinite Father had bestowed upon His Son, this princeof angels aspired to power which it was the prerogative of Christ alone to wield.

(7) WHAT IS THE RESULT OF REBELLION AGAINST GOD'S LAW?

____

____

Romans 6:23

All heaven had rejoiced to reflect the Creator's glory and to show forth His praise. And while God was thus honored, all had been peace and gladness. But a note of discord now marred the celestial harmonies. The service and exaltation of self, contrary to the Creator's plan, awakened forebodings of evil in minds to whom God's glory was supreme. The heavenly councils pleaded with Lucifer.

The Son of God presented before him the greatness, the goodness, and the justice of the Creator, and the sacred, unchanging nature of His law. God Himself had established the order of heaven; and in departing from it, Lucifer would dishonor his Maker, and bring ruin upon himself. But the warning, given in infinite love and mercy, only aroused a spirit of resistance. Lucifer allowed jealousy of Christ to prevail, and he became the more determined.

(8) WHAT DID LUCIFER'S SELF-PRIDE LEAD HIM TO DESIRE?

____

____

____

____

Isaiah 14:13,14

Pride in his own glory nourished the desire for supremacy. The high honors conferred upon Lucifer were not appreciated as the gift of God and called forth no gratitude to the Creator. He gloried in his brightness and exaltation, and aspired to be equal with God. He was beloved and reverenced by the heavenly host. Angels delighted to execute his commands, and he was clothed with wisdom and glory above them all. Yet the Son of God was the acknowledged Sovereign of heaven, one in power and authority with the Father. In all the councils of God, Christ was a participant, while Lucifer was not permitted thus to enter into the divine purposes. "Why," questioned this mighty angel, "should Christ have the supremacy? Why is He thus honored above Lucifer?"

(9) WHAT REPUTATION DID LUCIFER'S CONSPIRACY OF DECEPTION EARN FOR HIM?

____

____

John 8:44; Revelation 12:10

Leaving his place in the immediate presence of God, Lucifer went forth to diffuse the spirit of discontent among the angels. Working with mysterious secrecy, and for a time concealing his real purpose under an appearance of reverence for God, he endeavored to excite dissatisfaction concerning the laws that governed heavenly beings, intimating that they imposed an unnecessary restraint. Since their natures were holy, he urged that the angels should obey the dictates of their own will. He sought to create sympathy for himself by representing that God had dealt unjustly with him in bestowing supreme honor upon Christ. He claimed that in aspiring to greater power and honor he was not aiming at self-exaltation, but was seeking to secure liberty for all the inhabitants of heaven, that by this means they might attain to a higher state of existence.

(10) WHAT TRAITS OF CHARACTER DID GOD EXHIBIT IN DEALING WITH LUCIFER?

____

____

____

____

Romans 2:4

God in His great mercy bore long with Lucifer. He was not immediately degraded from his exalted station when he first indulged the spirit of discontent, nor even when he began to present his false claims before the loyal angels. Long was he retained in heaven. Again and again he was offered pardon on condition of repentance and submission. Such efforts as only infinite love and wisdom could devise were made to convince him of his error. The spirit of discontent had never before been known in heaven. Lucifer himself did not at first see whither he was drifting; he did not understand the real nature of his feelings. But as his dissatisfaction was proved to be without cause, Lucifer was convinced that he was in the wrong, that the divine claims were just, and that he ought to acknowledge them as such before all heaven. Had he done this, he might have saved himself and many angels. He had not at this time fully cast off his allegiance to God. Though he had forsaken his position as covering cherub, yet if he had been willing to return to God, acknowledging the Creator's wisdom, and satisfied to fill the place appointed him in God's great plan, he would have been reinstated in his office. But pride forbade him to submit. He persistently defended his own course, maintained that he had no need of repentance, and fully committed himself, in the great controversy, against his Maker.

(11) DURING HIS REBELLION HOW MANY ANGELS DID SATAN MANAGE TO DECEIVE?

____

____

____

Revelation 12:4

All the powers of his master mind were now bent to the work of deception, to secure the sympathy of the angels that had been under his command. Even the fact that Christ had warned and counseled him was perverted to serve his traitorous designs. To those whose loving trust bound them most closely to him, Satan had represented that he was wrongly judged, that his position was not respected, and that his liberty was to be abridged. From misrepresentation of the words of Christ he passed to prevarication and direct falsehood, accusing the Son of God of a design to humiliate him before the inhabitants of heaven. He sought also to make a false issue between himself and the loyal angels. All whom he could not subvert and bring fully to his side he accused of indifference to the interests of heavenly beings. The very work which he himself was doing he charged upon those who remained true to God. And to sustain his charge of God's injustice toward him, he resorted to misrepresentation of the words and acts of the Creator. It was his policy to perplex the angels with subtle arguments concerning the purposes of God. Everything that was simple he shrouded in mystery, and by artful perversion cast doubt upon the plainest statements of Jehovah. His high position, in such close connection with the divine administration, gave greater force to his representations, and many were induced to unite with him in rebellion against Heaven's authority.

(12) WHY DID GOD IN HIS INFINITE WISDOM ALLOW SATAN TO FULLY REVEAL HIS TRUE CHARACTER?

____

____

____

____

Proverbs 10:9; Numbers 32:23

God in His wisdom permitted Satan to carry forward his work, until the spirit of disaffection ripened into active revolt. It was necessary for his plans to be fully developed, that their true nature and tendency might be seen by all. Lucifer, as the anointed cherub, had been highly exalted; he was greatly loved by the heavenly beings, and his influence over them was strong. God's government included not only the inhabitants of heaven, but of all the worlds that He had created; and Satan thought that if he could carry the angels of heaven with him in rebellion, he could carry also the other worlds. He had artfully presented his side of the question, employing sophistry and fraud to secure his objects. His power to deceive was very great, and by disguising himself in a cloak of falsehood he had gained an advantage. Even the loyal angels could not fully discern his character or see to what his work was leading.

(13) WHY DIDN'T GOD DESTROY SATAN AT THE ONSET OF HIS REBELLION?

____

____

____

Job 37:23

Even when it was decided that he could no longer remain in heaven, Infinite Wisdom did not destroy Satan. Since the service of love can alone be acceptable to God, the allegiance of His creatures must rest upon a conviction of His justice and benevolence. The inhabitants of heaven and of other worlds, being unprepared to comprehend the nature or consequences of sin, could not then have seen the justice and mercy of God in the destruction of Satan. Had he been immediately blotted from existence, they would have served God from fear rather than from love. The influence of the deceiver would not have been fully destroyed, nor would the spirit of rebellion have been utterly eradicated. Evil must be permitted to come to maturity. For the good of the entire universe through ceaseless ages Satan must more fully develop his principles, that his charges against the divine government might be seen in their true light by all created beings, that the justice and mercy of God and the immutability of His law might forever be placed beyond all question.

Satan's rebellion was to be a lesson to the universe through all coming ages, a perpetual testimony to the nature and terrible results of sin. The working out of Satan's rule, its effects upon both men and angels, would show what must be the fruit of setting aside the divine authority. It would testify that with the existence of God's government and His law is bound up the well-being of all the creatures He has made. Thus the history of this terrible experiment of rebellion was to be perpetual safeguard to all holy intelligences, to prevent them from being deceived as to the nature of transgression, to save them from committing sin and suffering its punishments.

(14) TO WHAT CATASTROPHIC EVENT DID SATAN'S REBELLION LEAD?

____

____

____

____

Revelation 12:7-9; Luke 10:18

To the very close of the controversy in heaven the great usurper continued to justify himself. When it was announced that with all his sympathizers he must be expelled from the abodes of bliss, then the rebel leader boldly avowed his contempt for the Creator's law. He reiterated his claim that angels needed no control, but should be left to follow their own will, which would ever guide them right. He denounced the divine statutes as a restriction of their liberty and declared that it was his purpose to secure the abolition of law; that, freed from this restraint, the hosts of heaven might enter upon a more exalted, more glorious state of existence.

(15) AFTER BEING CAST FROM HEAVEN, WHERE DID SATAN SEEK TO ESTABLISH HIS KINGDOM?

____

____

____

Revelation 12:9

The same spirit that prompted rebellion in heaven still inspires rebellion on earth. Satan has continued with men the same policy which he pursued with the angels. His spirit now reigns in the children of disobedience. Like him they seek to break down the restraints of the law of God and promise men liberty through transgression of its precepts. Reproof of sin still arouses the spirit of hatred and resistance. When God's messages of warning are brought home to the conscience, Satan leads men to justify themselves and to seek the sympathy of others in their course of sin. Instead of correcting their errors, they excite indignation against the reprover, as if he were the sole cause of difficulty. From the days of righteous Abel to our own time such is the spirit which has been displayed toward those who dare to condemn sin.

By the same misrepresentation of the character of God as he had practiced in heaven, causing Him to be regarded as severe and tyrannical, Satan induced man to sin. And having succeeded thus far, he declared that God's unjust restrictions had led to man's fall, as they had led to his own rebellion.

(16) WHAT IS THE TRUE NATURE OF GOD'S CHARACTER?

____

____

____

Exodus 34:6,7

(17) HOW DID GOD DEMONSTRATE HIS GREAT LOVE AND MERCY?

____

____

____

John 3:16

In the banishment of Satan from heaven, God declared His justice and maintained the honor of His throne. But when man had sinned through yielding to the deceptions of this apostate spirit, God gave an evidence of His love by yielding up His only-begotten Son to die for the fallen race. In the atonement the character of God is revealed. The mighty argument of the cross demonstrates to the whole universe that the course of sin which Lucifer had chosen was in no wise chargeable upon the government of God.

(18) HOW DID EVIL MEN VERBALIZE SATAN'S MALICIOUS INTENT TO DESTROY JESUS DURING HIS EARTHLY MINISTRY?

____

____

____

Mark 15:13

In the contest between Christ and Satan, during the Saviour's earthly ministry, the character of the great deceiver was unmasked. Nothing could so effectually have uprooted Satan from the affections of the heavenly angels and the whole loyal universe as did his cruel warfare upon the world's Redeemer. The daring blasphemy of his demand that Christ should pay him homage, his presumptuous boldness in bearing Him to the mountain summit and the pinnacle of the temple, the malicious intent betrayed in urging Him to cast Himself down from the dizzy height, the unsleeping malice that hunted Him from place to place, inspiring the hearts of priests and people to reject His love, and at the last to cry, "Crucify Him! crucify Him!—all this excited the amazement and indignation of the universe.

Now the guilt of Satan stood forth without excuse. He had revealed his true character as a liar and a murderer. It was seen that the very same spirit with which he ruled the children of men, who were under his power, he would have manifested had he been permitted to control the inhabitants of heaven. He had claimed that the transgression of God's law would bring liberty and exaltation; but it was seen to result in bondage and degradation.

(19) WHAT DID GOD ACCOMPLISH BY THE SACRIFICE OF HIS SON THAT REVEALED HIS CHARACTER TO THE UNIVERSE?

____

____

____

____

2 Corinthians 5:18

God had manifested His abhorrence of the principles of rebellion. All heaven saw His justice revealed, both in the condemnation of Satan and in the redemption of man. Lucifer had declared that if the law of God was changeless, and its penalty could not be remitted, every transgressor must be forever debarred from the Creator's favor. He had claimed that the sinful race were placed beyond redemption and were therefore his rightful prey. But the death of Christ was an argument in man's behalf that could not be overthrown. The penalty of the law fell upon Him who was equal with God, and man was free to accept the righteousness of Christ and by a life of penitence and humiliation to triumph, as the Son of God had triumphed, over the power of Satan. Thus God is just and yet the justifier of all who believe in Jesus.

(20) WHAT WAS THE SPECIFIC MISSION OF CHRIST?

____

____

Matthew 5:17

But it was not merely to accomplish the redemption of man that Christ came to the earth to suffer and to die. He came to "magnify the law" and to "make it honorable." Not alone that the inhabitants of this world might regard the law as it should be regarded; but it was to demonstrate to all the worlds of the universe that God's law is unchangeable. Could its claims have been set aside, then the Son of God need not have yielded up His life to atone for its transgression. The death of Christ proves it immutable. And the sacrifice to which infinite love impelled the Father and the Son, that sinners might be redeemed, demonstrates to all the universe—what nothing less than this plan of atonement could have sufficed to do—that justice and mercy are the foundation of the law and government of God.

(21) AT THE CLOSE OF THE GREAT CONTROVERSY WHAT WILL BE THE CONFESSION OF EVERY CREATED BEING?

____

____

____

____

Philippians 2:10,11

In the final execution of the judgment it will be seen that no cause for sin exists. When the Judge of all the earth shall demand of Satan, "Why hast thou rebelled against Me, and robbed Me of the subjects of My kingdom?" The originator of evil can render no excuse. Every mouth will be stopped, and all the hosts of rebellion will be speechless.

(22) WHAT CRY PROCLAIMED THE IMPENDING DOOM OF SATAN?

____

____

____

John 19:30

The cross of Calvary, while it declares the law immutable, proclaims to the universe that the wages of sin is death. In the Saviour's expiring cry, "It is finished," the death knell of Satan was rung. The great controversy which had been so long in progress was then decided, and the final eradication of evil was made certain. The Son of God passed through the portals of the tomb, that "through death He might destroy him that had the power of death, that is, the devil." Hebrews 2:14.

(23) WHAT IS THE ULTIMATE FATE OF SATAN AND ALL WHO CLING TO PRIDE AND WICKEDNESS?

____

____

____

____

Malachi 4:1

Lucifer's desire for self-exaltation had led him to say: "I will exalt my throne above the stars of God: . . . I will be like the Most High." God declares: "I will bring thee to ashes upon the earth, . . . and never shalt thou be any more." Isaiah 14:13, 14; Ezekiel 28:18,19.

(24) AT THE CLOSE OF THE GREAT CONTROVERSY WHAT PROMISE WILL THE UNIVERSE CLAIM?

____

____

____

Nahum1:9

The whole universe will have become witnesses to the nature and results of sin. And its utter extermination, which in the beginning would have brought fear to angels and dishonor to God, will now vindicate His love and establish His honor before the universe of beings who delight to do His will, and in whose heart is His law. Never will evil again be manifest. Says the word of God: "Affliction shall not rise up the second time." The law of God, which Satan has reproached as the yoke of bondage, will be honored as the law of liberty. A tested and proved creation will never again be turned from allegiance to Him whose character has been fully manifested before them as fathomless love and infinite wisdom.

I understand how, by the pride of self, sin was first conceived in the heart of Lucifer. I know that at that moment God could have destroyed him but to do so, all His created beings would have obeyed out of fear.

Circle: Yes Undecided

I have experienced the misery that violation of God's love-based principles bring. I see love, fairness and mercy demonstrated by their obedience.

Circle: Yes Undecided

I now understand that in wisdom God allowed sin to run its malignant course so the entire universe could witness its terrible effects and see the true character of Satan.

Circle: Yes Undecided

I want to claim the great mercy God has provided by the sacrifice of His Son. I am glad that through this gift the requirements of the law are met. In His wisdom He remains just and the Justifier of all who believe.

Circle: Yes Undecided

Study Notes: ______________________________

Enmity Between Man and Satan - 2

(1) WHAT GREAT PROMISE WAS GIVEN BY GOD FOR THE HOPE OF FALLEN MAN?

____

____

____

____

____

Genesis 3:15

The divine sentence pronounced against Satan after the fall of man was also a prophecy, embracing all the ages to the close of time and foreshadowing the great conflict to engage all the races of men who should live upon the earth. God declares: "I will put enmity." This enmity is not naturally entertained. When man transgressed the divine law, his nature became evil, and he was in harmony, and not at variance, with Satan. There exists naturally no enmity between sinful man and the originator of sin. Both became evil through apostasy. The apostate is never at rest, except as he obtains sympathy and support by inducing others to follow his example. For this reason fallen angels and wicked men unite in desperate companionship. Had not God specially interposed, Satan and man would have entered into an alliance against Heaven; and instead of cherishing enmity against Satan, the whole human family would have been united in opposition to God.

(2) WHAT WAS GOD'S SPECIFIC COMMAND AND WARNING TO ADAM AND EVE?

____

____

____

Genesis 2:17

(3) WHAT ACT OF DEFIANCE BROUGHT DESTRUCTION TO THE EARTH AND A FALLEN NATURE TO ALL MANKIND?

____

____

____

Genesis 3:6

(4) WHAT IS TEMPTATION?

____

____

____

James 1:2,3

(5) WHO IS THE AUTHOR OF ALL TEMPTATION?

____

____

____

Luke 4:13

Satan tempted man to sin, as he had caused angels to rebel, that he might thus secure cooperation in his warfare against Heaven. There was no dissension between himself and the fallen angels as regards their hatred of Christ; while on all other points there was discord, they were firmly united in opposing the authority of the Ruler of the universe. But when Satan heard the declaration that enmity should exist between himself and the woman, and between his seed and her seed, he knew that his efforts to deprave human nature would be interrupted; that by some means man was to be enabled to resist his power.

(6) WHY IS SATAN DETERMINED TO DESTROY MANKIND?

____

____

____

Genesis 1:27

Satan's enmity against the human race is kindled because, through Christ, they are the objects of God's love and mercy. He desires to thwart the divine plan for man's redemption, to cast dishonor upon God, by defacing and defiling His handiwork; he would cause grief in heaven and fill the earth with woe and desolation. And he points to all this evil as the result of God's work in creating man.

(7) WHAT PRECIOUS PROMISE MAY WE CLAIM AND RECEIVE BY THE POWER OF CHRIST?

____

____

____

2 Peter 1:4

It is the grace that Christ implants in the soul which creates in man enmity against Satan. Without this converting grace and renewing power, man would continue the captive of Satan, a servant ever ready to do his bidding. But the new principle in the soul creates conflict where hitherto had been peace. The power which Christ imparts enables man to resist the tyrant and usurper. Whoever is seen to abhor sin instead of loving it, whoever resists and conquers those passions that have held sway within, displays the operation of a principle wholly from above.

(8) WHAT GODLY TRAIT OF CHRIST'S LIFE EVOKED ENMITY IN THE HEARTS OF THE UNGODLY TO THE POINT THAT THEY CRUCIFIED HIM?

___

___

1 John 3:5

The antagonism that exists between the spirit of Christ and the spirit of Satan was most strikingly displayed in the world's reception of Jesus. It was not so much because He appeared without worldly wealth, pomp, or grandeur that the Jews were led to reject Him. They saw that He possessed power which would more than compensate for the lack of these outward advantages. But the purity and holiness of Christ called forth against Him the hatred of the ungodly. His life of self-denial and sinless devotion was a perpetual reproof to a proud, sensual people. It was this that evoked enmity against the Son of God. Satan and evil angels joined with evil men. All the energies of apostasy conspired against the Champion of truth.

(9) WHAT TREATMENT CAN WE EXPECT FROM THE WORLD AS CHRIST'S FOLLOWERS?

___

___

___

2 Timothy 3:12

The same enmity is manifested toward Christ's followers as was manifested toward their Master. Whoever sees the repulsive character of sin, and in strength from above resists temptation, will assuredly arouse the wrath of Satan and his subjects. Hatred of the pure principles of truth, and reproach and persecution of its advocates, will exist as long as sin and sinners remain. The followers of Christ and the servants of Satan cannot harmonize. The offense of the cross has not ceased.

(10) WHAT TWO STEPS MUST WE FOLLOW TO OVERCOME THE FORCES OF SATAN?

___

___

___

James 4:7

Satan summons all his forces and throws his whole power into the combat. Why is it that he meets with no greater resistance? Why are the soldiers of Christ so sleepy and indifferent? Because they have so little real connection with Christ; because they are so destitute of His Spirit. Sin is not to them repulsive and abhorrent, as it was to their Master. They do not meet it, as did Christ, with decisive and determined resistance. They do not realize the exceeding evil and malignity of sin, and they are blinded both to the character and the power of the prince of darkness. There is little enmity against Satan and his works, because there is so great ignorance concerning his power and malice, and the vast extent of his warfare against Christ and His church. Multitudes are deluded here. They do not know that their enemy is a mighty general who controls the minds of evil angels, and that with well-matured plans and skillful movements he is warring against Christ to prevent the salvation of souls. Among professed Christians, and even among ministers of the gospel, there is heard scarcely a reference to Satan, except perhaps an incidental mention in the pulpit. They overlook the evidences of his continual activity and success; they neglect the many warnings of his subtlety; they seem to ignore his very existence.

(11) WHAT IS SATAN'S CONSTANT OBJECTIVE?

____

____

____

2 Corinthians 4:4

While men are ignorant of his devices, this vigilant foe is upon their track every moment. He is intruding his presence in every department of the household, in every street of our cities, in the churches, in the national councils, in the courts of justice, perplexing, deceiving, seducing, everywhere ruining the souls and bodies of men, women, and children, breaking up families, sowing hatred, emulation, strife, sedition, murder. And the Christian world seem to regard these things as though God had appointed them and they must exist.

Satan is continually seeking to overcome the people of God by breaking down the barriers which separate them from the world. Ancient Israel were enticed into sin when they ventured into forbidden association with the heathen. In a similar manner are modern Israel led astray. . . All who are not decided followers of Christ are servants of Satan. In the unregenerate heart there is love of sin and a disposition to cherish and excuse it. In the renewed heart there is hatred of sin and determined resistance against it. When Christians choose the society of the ungodly and unbelieving, they expose themselves to temptation. Satan conceals himself from view and stealthily draws his deceptive covering over their eyes. They cannot see that such company is calculated to do them harm; and while all the time assimilating to the world in character, words, and actions, they are becoming more and more blinded.

(12) HOW ONLY WILL WE BE SAFE FROM CONFORMITY TO THE WORLD?

____

____

____

____

Proverbs 4:14

Conformity to worldly customs converts the church to the world; it never converts the world to Christ. Familiarity with sin will inevitably cause it to appear less repulsive. He who chooses to associate with the servants of Satan will soon cease to fear their master. When in the way of duty we are brought into trial, as was Daniel in the King's court, we may be sure that God will protect us; but if we place ourselves under temptation we shall fall sooner or later.

(13) WHO ARE WE WARNED NOT TO FOLLOW OR MAKE THE FOCUS OF OUR ADMIRATION?

____

____

____

Proverbs 24:1; Psalms 37:1

The tempter often works most successfully through those who are least suspected of being under his control. The possessors of talent and education are admired and honored, as if these qualities could atone for the absence of the fear of God or entitle men to His favor. Talent and culture, considered in themselves, are gifts of God; but when these are made to supply the place of piety, when, instead of bringing the soul nearer to God, they lead away from Him, then they become a curse and a snare. The opinion prevails with many that all which appears like courtesy or refinement must, in some sense, pertain to Christ. Never was there a greater mistake. These qualities should grace the character of every Christian, for they would exert a powerful influence in favor of true religion; but they must be consecrated to God, or they also are a power for evil. Many a man of cultured intellect and pleasant manners, who would not stoop to what is commonly regarded as an immoral act, is but a polished instrument in the hands of Satan. The insidious, deceptive character of his influence and example renders him a more dangerous enemy to the cause of Christ than are those who are ignorant and uncultured.

(14) WHO IS THE ONLY SOURCE OF WISDOM AND SPIRITUAL STRENGTH?

____

____

Psalms 46:1

By earnest prayer and dependence upon God, Solomon obtained the wisdom which excited the wonder and admiration of the world. But when he turned from the Source of his strength, and went forward relying upon himself, he fell a prey to temptation. Then the marvelous powers bestowed on this wisest of kings only rendered him a more effective agent of the adversary of souls.

(15) WHAT STRATEGY HAS SATAN EMPLOYED IN HIS EFFORT TO WIN THE GREAT CONTROVERSY?

____

____

____

____

1 Peter 5:8

From the days of Adam to our own time, our great enemy has been exercising his power to oppress and destroy. He is now preparing for his last campaign against the church. All who seek to follow Jesus will be brought into conflict with this relentless foe. The more nearly the Christian imitates the divine Pattern, the more surely will he make himself a mark for the attacks of Satan. All who are actively engaged in the cause of God, seeking to unveil the deceptions of the evil one and to present Christ before the people, will be able to join in the testimony of Paul, in which he speaks of serving the Lord with all humility of mind, with many tears and temptations.

(16) WHAT WILL PROTECT US FROM THE WILES OF THE DEVIL?

____

____

____

____

Ephesians 6:11

Satan assailed Christ with his fiercest and most subtle temptations, but he was repulsed in every conflict. Those battles were fought in our behalf; those victories make it possible for us to conquer. Christ will give strength to all who seek it. No man without his own consent can be overcome by Satan. The tempter has no power to control the will or to force the soul to sin. He may distress, but he cannot contaminate. He can cause agony, but not defilement. The fact that Christ has conquered should inspire His followers with courage to fight manfully the battle against sin and Satan.

(17) HOW CAN OUR LIVES BE KEPT FREE FROM DEFILEMENT?

____

____

Psalms 119:9

> *I am grateful that God gave the promise to put enmity in the hearts of His children towards Satan.*
>
> **Circle: Yes Undecided**
>
> *I pray for spiritual wisdom and a greater desire for God's Word and, by His grace, I am determined to resist the advances of the devil.*
>
> **Circle: Yes Undecided**

(18) WHAT PROMISE FROM GOD CAN WE CLAIM?

____

____

____

____

____

____

____

1 Corinthians 10:13

> *I claim God's promise to not allow me to be tempted above what I am able to bear and pray for wisdom to choose the way of escape.*
>
> **Circle: Yes Undecided**
>
> *I realize that all those who live for Christ may suffer persecution and I am willing to bear it in love for Him.*
>
> **Circle: Yes Undecided**

Study Notes: ______________________________

____

____

____

____

____

____

____

____

____

Agency of Evil Spirits - 3

(1) HOW DOES SCRIPTURE IDENTIFY THE POWERS OF EVIL IN THE GREAT CONTROVERSY?

____

____

____

Ephesians 6:12

The connection of the visible with the invisible world, the ministration of angels of God, and the agency of evil spirits, are plainly revealed in the Scriptures, and inseparably interwoven with human history. There is a growing tendency to disbelief in the existence of evil spirits, while the holy angels that "minister for them who shall be heirs of salvation" (Hebrews 1:14) are regarded by many as spirits of the dead. But the Scriptures not only teach the existence of angels, both good and evil, but present unquestionable proof that these are not disembodied spirits of dead men.

(2) WHERE DID ALL ANGELS ABIDE BEFORE THE ONSET OF THE GREAT CONTROVERSY?

____

____

____

Revelation 5:11

(3) WHAT NAME IS USED IN SCRIPTURE IN REFERENCE TO THE FALLEN ANGELS?

____

____

____

Romans 8:38; Matthew 8:16,28,31;9:34

(4) WHERE DO THESE FALLEN BEINGS NOW ABIDE?

____

____

Revelation 12:9

(5) UPON WHAT LEVEL WAS MAN CREATED RELATIVE TO ANGELS?

____

____

____

Psalms 8:5; Hebrews 2:7

Before the creation of man, angels were in existence; for when the foundations of the earth were laid, "the morning stars sang together, and all the sons of God shouted for joy." Job 38:7. After the fall of man, angels were sent to guard the tree of life, and this before a human being had died. Angels are in nature superior to men, for the psalmist says that man was made "a little lower than the angels."

(6) HOW DOES SCRIPTURE DESCRIBE THE NUMBER OF ANGELS GOD CREATED?

____

____

Revelation 5:11

We are informed in Scripture as to the number, and the power and glory, of the heavenly beings, of their connection with the government of God, and also of their relation to the work of redemption. "The Lord hath prepared His throne in the heavens; and His kingdom ruleth over all." And, says the prophet, "I heard the voice of many angels round about the throne." In the presence chamber of the King of kings they wait—"angels, that excel in strength," "ministers of His, that do His pleasure," "hearkening unto the voice of His word." Psalm 103:19-21; Revelation 5:11. Ten thousand times ten thousand and thousands of thousands, were the heavenly messengers beheld by the prophet Daniel. The apostle Paul declared them "an innumerable company." Daniel 7:10; Hebrews 12:22.

(7) HOW MANY ANGELS CHOSE THE COURSE OF EVIL?

____

____

Revelation 12:4

(8) WHAT IS THE PHYSICAL APPEARANCE OF ANGELS?

____

____

____

____

____

Ezekiel 1:13,14

As God's messengers they go forth, like "the appearance of a flash of lightning," ... so dazzling their glory, and so swift their flight. The angel that appeared at the Saviour's tomb, his countenance "like lightning, and his raiment white as snow," caused the keepers for fear of him to quake, and they "became as dead men." Matthew 28:3, 4.

(9) WHAT EVENT IN THIS TEXT REVEALS THE POWER THAT A SINGLE ANGEL OF GOD POSSESSES?

2 Kings 19:35; 2 Chronicles 32:21; Matthew 28:2-4

When Sennacherib, the haughty Assyrian, reproached and blasphemed God, and threatened Israel with destruction, "it came to pass that night, that the angel of the Lord went out, and smote in the camp of the Assyrians an hundred fourscore and five thousand." There were "cut off all the mighty men of valor, and the leaders and captains," from the army of Sennacherib. "So he returned with shame of face to his own land." 2 Kings 19:35; 2 Chronicles 32:21.

(10) WHAT ROLE DID GOD ENTRUST TO THE UNFALLEN ANGELS AFTER THE FALL OF MAN?

Hebrews 1:14

Angels are sent on missions of mercy to the children of God. To Abraham, with promises of blessing; to the gates of Sodom, to rescue righteous Lot from its fiery doom; to Elijah, as he was about to perish from weariness and hunger in the desert; to Elisha, with chariots and horses of fire surrounding the little town where he was shut in by his foes; to Daniel, while seeking divine wisdom in the court of a heathen king, or abandoned to become the lions' prey; to Peter, doomed to death in Herod's dungeon; to the prisoners at Philippi; to Paul and his companions in the night of tempest on the sea; to open the mind of Cornelius to receive the gospel; to dispatch Peter with the message of salvation to the Gentile stranger—thus holy angels have, in all ages, ministered to God's people.

(11) WHAT DO ANGELS DO FOR US PERSONALLY?

Psalms 34:7

A guardian angel is appointed to every follower of Christ. These heavenly watchers shield the righteous from the power of the wicked one. This Satan himself recognized when he said: "Doth Job fear God for nought? Hast not Thou made an hedge about him, and about his house, and about all that he hath on every side?" Job 1:9, 10. The agency by which God protects His people is presented in the words of the psalmist: "The angel of the Lord encampeth round about them that fear Him, and delivereth them." Psalm 34:7. Said the Saviour, speaking of those that believe in Him: "Take heed that ye despise not one of these little ones; for I say unto you, That in heaven their angels do always behold the face of My Father." Matthew 18:10. The angels appointed to minister to the children of God have at all times access to His presence.

Thus God's people, exposed to the deceptive power and unsleeping malice of the prince of darkness, and in conflict with all the forces of evil, are assured of the unceasing guardianship of heavenly angels. Nor is such assurance given without need. If God has granted to His children promise of grace and protection, it is because there are mighty agencies of evil to be met—agencies numerous, determined, and untiring, of whose malignity and power none can safely be ignorant or unheeding.

(12) WHAT CHANGED THE HOLY ANGELS INTO DEMONS?

____

____

2 Peter 2:4; Jude 6

Evil spirits, in the beginning created sinless, were equal in nature, power, and glory with the holy beings that are now God's messengers. But fallen through sin, they are leagued together for the dishonor of God and the destruction of men. United with Satan in his rebellion, and with him cast out from heaven, they have, through all succeeding ages, cooperate with him in his warfare against the divine authority. We are told in Scripture of their confederacy and government, of their various orders, of their intelligence and subtlety, and of their malicious designs against the peace and happiness of men.

(13) WHAT FEATS DOES SATAN EMPLOY TO DECEIVE AND CONTROL MANKIND?

____

____

Revelation 16:14

Old Testament history presents occasional mention of their existence and agency; but it was during the time when Christ was upon the earth that evil spirits manifested their power in the most striking manner. Christ had come to enter upon the plan devised for man's redemption, and Satan determined to assert his right to control the world.

(14) WHERE WILL THE FORCES OF EVIL ABIDE WHEN SINFUL MAN ALLOWS?

____

____

Matthew 8:16

The fact that men have been possessed with demons, is clearly stated in the New Testament. The persons thus afflicted were not merely suffering with disease from natural causes. Christ had perfect understanding of that with which He was dealing, and He recognized the direct presence and agency of evil spirits.

A striking example of their number, power, and malignity, and also of the power and mercy of Christ, is given in the Scripture account of the healing of the demoniacs at Gadara. Those wretched maniacs, spurning all restraint, writhing, foaming, raging, were filling the air with their cries, doing violence to themselves, and endangering all who should approach them. Their bleeding and disfigured bodies and distracted minds presented a spectacle well pleasing to the prince of darkness.

(15) HOW MANY DEMONS INHABITED THE MAN FROM THE COUNTRY OF THE GADARENES?

____

____

____

Mark 5:9

In the Roman army a legion consisted of from three to five thousand men. Satan's hosts also are marshaled in companies, and the single company to which these demons belonged numbered no less than a legion.

(16) BY THE POWER OF WHOSE NAME MUST THE FORCES OF EVIL FLEE?

Luke 10:17

At the command of Jesus the evil spirits departed from their victims, leaving them calmly sitting at the Saviour's feet, subdued, intelligent, and gentle. . . .

. . . It was also His will that the people of that region should behold His power to break the bondage of Satan and release his captives. And though Jesus Himself departed, the men so marvelously delivered, remained to declare the mercy of their Benefactor.

(17) WHAT WAS THE CHOSEN PROFESSION OF ELYMAS REVEALING THAT DEVIL POSSESSION CAN BE BY CHOICE?

Acts 13:8

Those possessed with devils are usually represented as being in a condition of great suffering; yet there were exceptions to this rule. For the sake of obtaining supernatural power, some welcomed the satanic influence. These of course had no conflict with the demons. Of this class were those who possessed the spirit of divination,—Simon Magus, Elymas the sorcerer, and the damsel who followed Paul and Silas at Philippi.

(18) HOW DOES THIS VERSE DESCRIBE THE PHYSICAL APPEARANCE OF LUCIFER–NOW CALLED SATAN?

Ezekiel 28:17

There is nothing that the great deceiver fears so much as that we shall become acquainted with his devices. The better to disguise his real character and purposes, he has caused himself to be so represented as to excite no stronger emotion than ridicule or contempt. He is well pleased to be painted as a ludicrous or loathsome object, misshapen, half animal and half human. He is pleased to hear his name used in sport and mockery by those who think themselves intelligent and well informed.

(19) WHAT ACTION DOES THE BIBLE TEACH THAT GIVES WISDOM TO PREVENT DECEPTION?

Ephesians 6:11

---

2 Timothy 2:15

It is because he has masked himself with consummate skill that the question is so widely asked: "Does such a being really exist?" It is an evidence of his success that theories giving the lie to the plainest testimony of the Scriptures are so generally received in the religious world. And it is because Satan can most readily control the minds of those who are unconscious of his influence, that the word of God gives us so many examples of his malignant work, unveiling before us his secret forces, and thus placing us on our guard against his assaults.

(20) WHAT GREAT PROMISE OF PROTECTION MAY WE CLAIM WHEN WE ARE ATTACKED BY THE FORCES OF EVIL?

____

____

____

Psalms 97:10

The power and malice of Satan and his host might justly alarm us were it not that we may find shelter and deliverance in the superior power of our Redeemer. We carefully secure our houses with bolts and locks to protect our property and our lives from evil men; but we seldom think of the evil angels who are constantly seeking access to us, and against whose attacks we have, in our own strength, no method of defense. If permitted, they can distract our minds, disorder and torment our bodies, destroy our possessions and our lives. Their only delight is in misery and destruction. Fearful is the condition of those who resist the divine claims and yield to Satan's temptations, until God gives them up to the control of evil spirits. But those who follow Christ are ever safe under His watchcare. Angels that excel in strength are sent from heaven to protect them. The wicked one cannot break through the guard which God has stationed about His people.

I understand from Scripture that I am caught in a cosmic struggle between good and evil. I realize the demonic powers are not spirits of dead humans but rather fallen angels seeking my destruction because I claim God's gift of grace.

Circle: Yes Undecided

I am thankful that God sends His unfallen heavenly messengers to minister to my needs and to provide protection during this great controversy.

Circle: Yes Undecided

I realize that I am no match for the intelligence, power, or abilities of Satan and his evil agents. I thank God I can claim the supernatural power in the name of Christ for deliverance from these forces of evil.

Circle: Yes Undecided

I know that in the last days the powers of darkness will use miraculous signs and wonders to deceive me. I pray for the Holy Spirit to guide my study of God's Word so I will not be deceived.

Circle: Yes Undecided

Study Notes: ______________________________

____

____

____

____

Snares of Satan - 4

(1) WHAT IS SATAN'S ULTIMATE GOAL IN THIS GREAT CONTROVERSY?

____

____

Revelation 20:3; John 10:10

The great controversy between Christ and Satan, that has been carried forward for nearly six thousand years, is soon to close; and the wicked one redoubles his efforts to defeat the work of Christ in man's behalf and to fasten souls in his snares. To hold the people in darkness and impenitence till the Saviour's mediation is ended, and there is no longer a sacrifice for sin, is the object which he seeks to accomplish.

(2) WHAT TWO-PART INSTRUCTION ARE WE GIVEN TO PROTECT US FROM SATAN'S DECEPTIONS?

____

____

____

James 4:7

When there is no special effort made to resist his power, when indifference prevails in the church and the world, Satan is not concerned; for he is in no danger of losing those whom he is leading captive at his will. But when the attention is called to eternal things, and souls are inquiring, "What must I do to be saved?" he is on the ground, seeking to match his power against the power of Christ and to counteract the influence of the Holy Spirit.

(3) WHAT BIBLICAL ADVICE WILL HELP US OVERCOME THE LUSTS OF THE FLESH?

____

____

____

Galations 5:16; 6:8

Again, Satan sees the Lord's servants burdened because of the spiritual darkness that enshrouds the people. He hears their earnest prayers for divine grace and power to break the spell of indifference, carelessness, and indolence. Then with renewed zeal he plies his arts. He tempts men to the indulgence of appetite or to some other form of self-gratification, and thus benumbs their sensibilities so that they fail to hear the very things which they most need to learn.

(4) WHAT ARE THE THREE MAIN DIVERSIONS SATAN IS USING TO DISTRACT OUR THOUGHTS FROM ETERNAL ISSUES?

____

____

____

____

____

Mark 4:19

Satan well knows that all whom he can lead to neglect prayer and the searching of the Scriptures, will be overcome by his attacks. Therefore he invents every possible device to engross the mind.

(5) HOW DOES SATAN USE THOSE WHO CLAIM TO BE CHRISTIANS BUT ARE NOT?

____

____

____

Romans 16:17

There has ever been a class professing godliness, who, instead of following on to know the truth, make it their religion to seek some fault of character or error of faith in those with whom they do not agree. Such are Satan's right-hand helpers. Accusers of the brethren are not few, and they are always active when God is at work and His servants are rendering Him true homage. They will put a false coloring upon the words and acts of those who love and obey the truth. They will represent the most earnest, zealous, self-denying servants of Christ as deceived or deceivers. It is their work to misrepresent the motives of every true and noble deed, to circulate insinuations, and arouse suspicion in the minds of the inexperienced. In every conceivable manner they will seek to cause that which is pure and righteous to be regarded as foul and deceptive.

(6) HOW DOES SCRIPTURE IDENTIFY THESE DECEIVERS?

____

____

____

Matthew 7:16

But none need be deceived concerning them. It may be readily seen whose children they are, whose example they follow, and whose work they do. . . Their course resembles that of Satan, the envenomed slanderer, "the accuser of our brethren." Revelation 12:10.

The great deceiver has many agents ready to present any and every kind of error to ensnare souls—heresies prepared to suit the varied tastes and capacities of those whom he would ruin. It is his plan to bring into the church insincere, unregenerate elements that will encourage doubt and unbelief, and hinder all who desire to see the work of God advance and to advance with it. Many who have no real faith in God or in His word assent to some principles of truth and pass as Christians, and thus they are enabled to introduce their errors as Scriptural doctrines.

(7) WHAT IS THE RESULT OF ACCEPTING TRUTH?

____

____

John 8:32

The position that it is of no consequence what men believe is one of Satan's most successful deceptions. He knows that the truth, received in the love of it, sanctifies the soul of the receiver; therefore he is constantly seeking to substitute false theories, fables, another gospel. From the beginning the servants of God have contended against false teachers, not merely as vicious men, but as inculcators of falsehoods that were fatal to the soul. Elijah, Jeremiah, Paul, firmly and fearlessly opposed those who were turning men from the word of God. That liberality which regards a correct religious faith as unimportant found no favor with these holy defenders of the truth.

(8) WHAT WILL HAPPEN TO THOSE WHO TWIST SCRIPTURE TO FIT THEIR BELIEFS?

____

____

____

____

2 Peter 3:16

The vague and fanciful interpretations of Scripture, and the many conflicting theories concerning religious faith, that are found in the Christian world are the work of our great adversary to confuse minds so that they shall not discern the truth. And the discord and division which exist among the churches of Christendom are in a great measure due to the prevailing custom of wresting the Scriptures to support a favorite theory. Instead of carefully studying God's word with humility of heart to obtain a knowledge of His will, many seek only to discover something odd or original.

(9) WHAT WARNING IS GIVEN TO THOSE WHO MIGHT THINK TO CHANGE THE MEANING OF GOD'S WORD?

____

____

____

____

Revelation 22:18

In order to sustain erroneous doctrines or unchristian practices, some will seize upon passages of Scripture separated from the context, perhaps quoting half of a single verse as proving their point, when the remaining portion would show the meaning to be quite the opposite. With the cunning of the serpent they entrench themselves behind disconnected utterances construed to suit their carnal desires. Thus do many willfully pervert the word of God. Others, who have an active imagination, seize upon the figures and symbols of Holy Writ, interpret them to suit their fancy, with little regard to the testimony of Scripture as its own interpreter, and then they present their vagaries as the teachings of the Bible.

Whenever the study of the Scriptures is entered upon without a prayerful, humble, teachable spirit, the plainest and simplest as well as the most difficult passages will be wrested from their true meaning.

(10) WHAT WILL THE TESTIMONY OF THE LORD DO FOR THE SIMPLEST MIND?

____

____

Psalms 19:7

The Bible was designed to be a guide to all who wish to become acquainted with the will of their Maker. God gave to men the sure word of prophecy; angels and even Christ Himself came to make known to Daniel and John the things that must shortly come to pass. Those important matters that concern our salvation were not left involved in mystery. They were not revealed in such a way as to perplex and mislead the honest seeker after truth. Said the Lord by the prophet Habakkuk: "Write the vision, and make it plain, . . . that he may run that readeth it." Habakkuk 2:2. The word of God is plain to all who study it with a prayerful heart. Every truly honest soul will come to the light of truth. "Light is sown for the righteous." Psalm 97:11.

(11) HOW DOES GOD VIEW THE WISDOM OF THIS WORLD?

____

____

1 Corinthians 3:19

To many, scientific research has become a curse. God has permitted a flood of light to be poured upon the world in discoveries in science and art; but even the greatest minds, if not guided by the word of God in their research, become bewildered in their attempts to investigate the relations of science and revelation.

(12) HOW DOES SCRIPTURE REGARD SECULAR SCIENCE?

____

____

____

1 Timothy 6:20

Human knowledge of both material and spiritual things is partial and imperfect; therefore many are unable to harmonize their views of science with Scripture statements. Many accept mere theories and speculations as scientific facts, and they think that God's word is to be tested by the teachings of "science falsely so called." . . . The Creator and His works are beyond their comprehension; and because they cannot explain these by natural laws, Bible history is regarded as unreliable. Those who doubt the reliability of the records of the Old and New Testaments too often go a step further and doubt the existence of God and attribute infinite power to nature. Having let go their anchor, they are left to beat about upon the rocks of infidelity.

(13) WHY WILL MAN NEVER FULLY UNDERSTAND GOD?

____

____

____

____

Romans 11:33

Thus many err from the faith and are seduced by the devil. Men have endeavored to be wiser than their Creator; human philosophy has attempted to search out and explain mysteries which will never be revealed through the eternal ages. If men would but search and understand what God had made known of Himself and His purposes, they would obtain such a view of the glory, majesty, and power of Jehovah that they would realize their own littleness and would be content with that which has been revealed for themselves and their children.

It is a masterpiece of Satan's deceptions to keep the minds of men searching and conjecturing in regard to that which God has not made known and which He does not intend that we shall understand. It was thus that Lucifer lost his place in heaven. He became dissatisfied because all the secrets of God's purposes were not confided to him, and he entirely disregarded that which was revealed concerning his own work in the lofty position assigned him. By arousing the same discontent in the angels under his command, he caused their fall. Now he seeks to imbue the minds of men with the same spirit and to lead them also to disregard the direct commands of God.

(14) WHO IS IN DANGER OF BELIEVING STRONG DELUSIONS?

____

____

____

____

2 Thessalonions 2:10-12

Those who are unwilling to accept the plain, cutting truths of the Bible are continually seeking for pleasing fables that will quiet the conscience. The less spiritual, self-denying, and humiliating the doctrines presented, the greater the favor with which they are received. These persons degrade the intellectual powers to serve their carnal desires. Too wise in their own conceit to search the Scriptures with contrition of soul and earnest prayer for divine guidance, they have no shield from delusion. Satan is ready to supply the heart's desire, and he palms off his deceptions in the place of truth. . . . All who neglect the word of God to study convenience and policy, that they may not be at variance with the world, will be left to receive damnable heresy for religious truth. Every conceivable form of error will be accepted by those who willfully reject the truth. He who looks with horror upon one deception will readily receive another.

Among the most successful agencies of the great deceiver are the delusive teachings and lying wonders of spiritualism. Disguised as an angel of light, he spreads his nets where least suspected. If men would but study the Book of God with earnest prayer that they might understand it, they would not be left in darkness to receive false doctrines. But as they reject the truth they fall a prey to deception.

(15) WHAT ARE WE INSTRUCTED TO AVOID?

____

____

____

Mark 7:13

Innumerable are the erroneous doctrines and fanciful ideas that are obtaining among the churches of Christendom. It is impossible to estimate the evil results of removing one of the landmarks fixed by the word of God. Few who venture to do this stop with the rejection of a single truth. The majority continue to set aside one after another of the principles of truth, until they become actual infidels.

The errors of popular theology have driven many a soul to skepticism who might otherwise have been a believer in the Scriptures. It is impossible for him to accept doctrines which outrage his sense of justice, mercy, and benevolence; and since these are represented as the teaching of the Bible, he refuses to receive it as the word of God.

(16) WHAT IS THE DANGER OF HOLDING IN GREAT ESTEEM THE TRADITIONS OF MAN?

____

____

____

Mark 7:9

And this is the object which Satan seeks to accomplish. There is nothing that he desires more than to destroy confidence in God and in His word. Satan stands at the head of the great army of doubters, and he works to the utmost of his power to beguile souls into his ranks. It is becoming fashionable to doubt. There is a large class by whom the word of God is looked upon with distrust for the same reason as was its Author—because it reproves and condemns sin. Those who are unwilling to obey its requirements endeavor to overthrow its authority. They read the Bible, or listen to its teachings as presented from the sacred desk, merely to find fault with the Scriptures or with the sermon. Not a few become infidels in order to justify or excuse themselves in neglect of duty. Others adopt skeptical principles from pride and indolence. Too ease-loving to distinguish themselves by accomplishing anything worthy of honor, which requires effort and self-denial, they aim to secure a reputation for superior wisdom by criticizing the Bible. There is much which the finite mind, unenlightened by divine wisdom, is powerless to comprehend; and thus they find occasion to criticize. There are many who seem to feel that it is a virtue to stand on the side of unbelief, skepticism, and infidelity. But underneath an appearance of candor it will be found that such persons are actuated by self-confidence and pride. Many delight in finding something in the Scriptures to puzzle the minds of others. Some at first criticize and reason on the wrong side, from a mere love of controversy. They do not realize that they are thus entangling themselves in the snare of the fowler. But having openly expressed unbelief, they feel that they must maintain their position. Thus they unite with the ungodly and close to themselves the gates of Paradise.

(17) WHO WILL BE GRANTED THE AID OF THE HOLY SPIRIT?

____

____

____

Luke 11:13

God has given in His word sufficient evidence of its divine character. The great truths which concern our redemption are clearly presented. By the aid of the Holy Spirit, which is promised to all who seek it in sincerity, every man may understand these truths for himself. God has granted to men a strong foundation upon which to rest their faith.

(18) WHAT GREAT PROMISE IN THIS VERSE MAY WE CLAIM?

Psalms 118:8

Yet the finite minds of men are inadequate fully to comprehend the plans and purposes of the Infinite One. We can never by searching find out God. We must not attempt to lift with presumptuous hand the curtain behind which He veils His majesty. . . . We can so far comprehend His dealings with us, and the motives by which He is actuated, that we may discern boundless love and mercy united to infinite power. Our Father in heaven orders everything in wisdom and righteousness, and we are not to be dissatisfied and distrustful, but to bow in reverent submission. He will reveal to us as much of His purposes as it is for our good to know, and beyond that we must trust the Hand that is omnipotent, the Heart that is full of love.

(19) WHAT IS THE DANGEROUS FRUIT OF UNBELIEF?

Hebrews 3:12,13

While God has given ample evidence for faith, He will never remove all excuse for unbelief. All who look for hooks to hang their doubts upon will find them. And those who refuse to accept and obey God's word until every objection has been removed, and there is no longer an opportunity for doubt, will never come to the light.

(20) WHAT IS THE NATURAL RESPONSE FROM A CARNAL MIND?

Matthew 14:31

Distrust of God is the natural outgrowth of the unrenewed heart, which is at enmity with Him. But faith is inspired by the Holy Spirit, and it will flourish only as it is cherished. No man can become strong in faith without a determined effort. Unbelief strengthens as it is encouraged; and if men, instead of dwelling upon the evidences which God has given to sustain their faith, permit themselves to question and cavil, they will find their doubts constantly becoming more confirmed.

(21) WHAT BIBLICAL PRINCIPLE WILL FOLLOW THOSE WHO DOUBT AND DISTRUST GOD?

Galations 6:7

But those who doubt God's promises and distrust the assurance of His grace are dishonoring Him; and their influence, instead of drawing others to Christ, tends to repel them from Him. They are unproductive trees, that spread their dark branches far and wide, shutting away the sunlight from other plants, and causing them to droop and die under the chilling shadow. The lifework of these persons will appear as a never-ceasing witness against them. They are sowing seeds of doubt and skepticism that will yield an unfailing harvest.

(22) WHAT IS THE FIRST STEP TO FREEDOM FROM DOUBT OF DOCTRINE?

____

____

____

John 7:17; 1 John 1:7

There is but one course for those to pursue who honestly desire to be freed from doubts. Instead of questioning and caviling concerning that which they do not understand, let them give heed to the light which already shines upon them, and they will receive greater light. Let them do every duty which has been made plain to their understanding, and they will be enabled to understand and perform those of which they are now in doubt.

(23) WHAT TWO KEYS ARE AVAILABLE TO US FOR RECEIVING STRONGER FAITH?

____

____

Romans 10:17

____

____

____

Mark 9:24

(24) WHAT IS PROMISED TO THOSE WHO SEEK?

____

____

____

Matthew 7:7

Satan can present a counterfeit so closely resembling the truth that it deceives those who are willing to be deceived, who desire to shun the self-denial and sacrifice demanded by the truth; but it is impossible for him to hold under his power one soul who honestly desires, at whatever cost, to know the truth. Christ is the truth and the "Light, which lighteth every man that cometh into the world." John 1:9. The Spirit of truth has been sent to guide men into all truth.

(25) WHY DOES GOD ALLOW US TO UNDERGO TEMPTATION?

____

____

____

Job 23:10; 1 Peter 1:7

The followers of Christ know little of the plots which Satan and his hosts are forming against them. But He who sitteth in the heavens will overrule all these devices for the accomplishment of His deep designs. The Lord permits His people to be subjected to the fiery ordeal of temptation, not because He takes pleasure in their distress and affliction, but because this process is essential to their final victory. He could not, consistently with His own glory, shield them from temptation; for the very object of the trial is to prepare them to resist all the allurements of evil.

(26) FROM WHOM WILL POWER TO RESIST TEMPTATION COME?

____

____

____

Zechariah 4:6

Neither wicked men nor devils can hinder the work of God, or shut out His presence from His people, if they will, with subdued, contrite hearts, confess and put away their sins, and in faith claim His promises. Every temptation, every opposing influence, whether open or secret, may be successfully resisted . . .

(27) WHY DO WE NOT HAVE TO FEAR THE POWERS OF EVIL?

____

____

____

Luke 10:19

Satan is well aware that the weakest soul who abides in Christ is more than a match for the hosts of darkness, and that, should he reveal himself openly, he would be met and resisted. Therefore he seeks to draw away the soldiers of the cross from their strong fortification, while he lies in ambush with his forces, ready to destroy all who venture upon his ground. Only in humble reliance upon God, and obedience to all His commandments, can we be secure.

(28) WHAT TWO PROVISIONS DID JESUS GIVE TO PREVENT US FROM ENTERING INTO TEMPTATION?

____

____

Matthew 26:41; Mark 13:33

No man is safe for a day or an hour without prayer. Especially should we entreat the Lord for wisdom to understand His word. Here are revealed the wiles of the tempter and the means by which he may be successfully resisted. Satan is an expert in quoting Scripture, placing his own interpretation upon passages, by which he hopes to cause us to stumble. We should study the Bible with humility of heart, never losing sight of our dependence upon God. While we must constantly guard against the devices of Satan, we should pray in faith continually: "Lead us not into temptation."

I realize Satan's goal is to deceive the world and he will use every method in His power to bring about my ruin. I am thankful for the promise that if I sincerely seek wisdom and truth I will find it and not fall to his deceptions.

Circle: Yes Undecided

I understand that Satan uses both professing believers and nonbelievers alike as his tools to lead me astray. My prayer is: "Lord, please give me wisdom to discern these satanic influences."

Circle: Yes Undecided

I pray for determination to continually follow Christ's warning and not give in to the temptation of seeking worldly wealth which would draw me away from my relationship with Him.

Circle: Yes Undecided

I am thankful for the promises that God will give us power over evil and never allow me to be tempted above what I am able to bear. I pray that, by faith and His grace, I can overcome and give glory to His name.

Circle: Yes Undecided

The First Great Deception - 5

With the earliest history of man, Satan began his efforts to deceive our race. He who had incited rebellion in heaven desired to bring the inhabitants of the earth to unite with him in his warfare against the government of God. Adam and Eve had been perfectly happy in obedience to the law of God, and this fact was a constant testimony against the claim which Satan had urged in heaven, that God's law was oppressive and opposed to the good of His creatures. And furthermore, Satan's envy was excited as he looked upon the beautiful home prepared for the sinless pair. He determined to cause their fall, that, having separated them from God and brought them under his own power, he might gain possession of the earth and here establish his kingdom in opposition to the Most High.

(1) WHY IS IMMEDIATE UNYIELDING OBEDIENCE TO GOD'S WILL ESSENTIAL?

____

____

____

Romans 6:16

Had Satan revealed himself in his real character, he would have been repulsed at once, for Adam and Eve had been warned against this dangerous foe; but he worked in the dark, concealing his purpose, that he might more effectually accomplish his object. Employing as his medium the serpent, then a creature of fascinating appearance, he addressed himself to Eve: "Hath God said, Ye shall not eat of every tree of the garden?" Genesis 3:1. Had Eve refrained from entering into argument with the tempter, she would have been safe; but she ventured to parley with him and fell a victim to his wiles. It is thus that many are still overcome. They doubt and argue concerning the requirements of God; and instead of obeying the divine commands, they accept human theories, which but disguise the devices of Satan.

(2) WHAT GREAT DECEPTION DID ADAM AND EVE CHOOSE TO BELIEVE?

____

____

____

Genesis 3:4

"The woman said unto the serpent, We may eat of the fruit of the trees of the garden: but of the fruit of the tree which is in the midst of the garden, God hath said, Ye shall not eat of it, neither shall ye touch it, lest ye die. And the serpent said unto the woman, Ye shall not surely die: for God doth know that in the day ye eat thereof, then your eyes shall be opened, and ye shall be as gods, knowing good and evil." Verses 2-5. He declared that they would become like God, possessing greater wisdom than before and being capable of a higher state of existence. Eve yielded to temptation; and through her influence, Adam was led into sin. They accepted the words of the serpent, that God did not mean what He said; they distrusted their Creator and imagined that He was restricting their liberty and that they might obtain great wisdom and exaltation by transgressing His law.

(3) WHAT WAS THE IMMEDIATE RESULT OF THEIR TRANSGRESSION?

____

____

____

Isaiah 59:2

____

____

____

Genesis 3:22,23

(4) WHAT IS SIN?

____

____

____

1 John 3:4

(5) WHAT IS THE ULTIMATE RESULT OF SIN?

____

____

____

Romans 6:23

But what did Adam, after his sin, find to be the meaning of the words, "In the day that thou eatest thereof thou shalt surely die"? Did he find them to mean, as Satan had led him to believe, that he was to be ushered into a more exalted state of existence? Then indeed there was great good to be gained by transgression, and Satan was proved to be a benefactor of the race. But Adam did not find this to be the meaning of the divine sentence. God declared that as a penalty for his sin, man should return to the ground whence he was taken: "Dust thou art, and unto dust shalt thou return." Verse 19. The words of Satan, "Your eyes shall be opened," proved to be true in this sense only: After Adam and Eve had disobeyed God, their eyes were opened to discern their folly; they did know evil, and they tasted the bitter fruit of transgression.

In the midst of Eden grew the tree of life, whose fruit had the power of perpetuating life. Had Adam remained obedient to God, he would have continued to enjoy free access to this tree and would have lived forever. But when he sinned he was cut off from partaking of the tree of life, and he became subject to death. The divine sentence, "Dust thou art, and unto dust shalt thou return," points to the utter extinction of life.

(6) WHAT IS MAN'S ONLY HOPE OF REGAINING IMMORTALITY?

____

____

____

____

____

2 Timothy 1:10; Romans 5:12-15

Immortality, promised to man on condition of obedience, had been forfeited by transgression. Adam could not transmit to his posterity that which he did not possess; and there could have been no hope for the fallen race had not God, by the sacrifice of His Son, brought immortality within their reach. . . . And only through Christ can immortality be obtained. Said Jesus: "He that believeth on the Son hath everlasting life: and he that believeth not the Son shall not see life." John 3:36. Every man may come into possession of this priceless blessing if he will comply with the conditions. All "who by patient continuance in well-doing seek for glory and honor and immortality," will receive "eternal life." Romans 2:7.

(7) WHAT HAPPENS TO THE SOUL OF A SINNER?

____

____

____

Genesis 2:17; Ezekiel 18:20,4

The only one who promised Adam life in disobedience was the great deceiver. And the declaration of the serpent to Eve in Eden—"Ye shall not surely die"—was the first sermon ever preached upon the immortality of the soul. Yet this declaration, resting solely upon the authority of Satan, is echoed from the pulpits of Christendom and is received by the majority of mankind as readily as it was received by our first parents. The divine sentence, "The soul that sinneth, it shall die" (Ezekiel 18:20), is made to mean: The soul that sinneth, it shall not die, but live eternally. We cannot but wonder at the strange infatuation which renders men so credulous concerning the words of Satan and so unbelieving in regard to the words of God.

(8) HOW DID GOD PREVENT THE IMMORTALIZATION OF SIN AND SINNERS?

____

____

____

Genesis 3:24

Had man after his fall been allowed free access to the tree of life, he would have lived forever, and thus sin would have been immortalized. But cherubim and a flaming sword kept "the way of the tree of life" and not one of the family of Adam has been permitted to pass that barrier and partake of the life-giving fruit. Therefore there is not an immortal sinner.

(9) WHAT HAPPENS TO THE BODY AND SOUL OF THE WICKED AFTER THE FINAL JUDGEMENT?

___

___

___

Matthew 10:28

(10) HOW DOES THE LORD FEEL ABOUT THE DESTRUCTION OF THOSE WHO REJECT SALVATION?

___

___

___

Ezekiel 33:11

___

___

___

2 Peter 3:9

But after the Fall, Satan bade his angels make a special effort to inculcate the belief in man's natural immortality; and having induced the people to receive this error, they were to lead them on to conclude that the sinner would live in eternal misery. Now the prince of darkness, working through his agents, represents God as a revengeful tyrant, declaring that He plunges into hell all those who do not please Him, and causes them ever to feel His wrath; and that while they suffer unutterable anguish and writhe in the eternal flames, their Creator looks down upon them with satisfaction. Thus the archfiend clothes with his own attributes the Creator and Benefactor of mankind. Cruelty is satanic. God is love; and all that He created was pure, holy, and lovely, until sin was brought in by the first great rebel. Satan himself is the enemy who tempts man to sin, and then destroys him if he can; and when he has made sure of his victim, then he exults in the ruin he has wrought. If permitted, he would sweep the entire race into his net. Were it not for the interposition of divine power, not one son or daughter of Adam would escape.

(11) WHAT FOUR ATTRIBUTES DESCRIBE THE TRUE CHARACTER AND GOVERNMENT OF GOD?

___

___

___

___

Psalm 89:14

Satan is seeking to overcome men today, as he overcame our first parents, by shaking their confidence in their Creator and leading them to doubt the wisdom of His government and the justice of His laws. Satan and his emissaries represent God as even worse than themselves, in order to justify their own malignity and rebellion. The great deceiver endeavors to shift his own horrible cruelty of character upon our heavenly Father, that he may cause himself to appear as one greatly wronged by his expulsion from heaven because he would not submit to so unjust a governor. He presents before the world the liberty which they may enjoy under his mild sway, in contrast with the bondage imposed by the stern decrees of Jehovah. Thus he succeeds in luring souls away from their allegiance to God.

(12) WHAT WILL REMAIN OF THE WICKED WHEN JUST PUNISHMENT HAS BEEN DELIVERED?

____

____

Malachi 4:3; Psalm 37:20; Obadiah 1:16

How repugnant to every emotion of love and mercy, and even to our sense of justice, is the doctrine that the wicked dead are tormented with fire and brimstone in an eternally burning hell; that for the sins of a brief earthly life they are to suffer torture as long as God shall live. Yet this doctrine has been widely taught and is still embodied in many of the creeds of Christendom. . . .

(13) HOW DOES SATAN COME TO HIS END?

____

____

____

____

Ezekiel 28:18

What would be gained to God should we admit that He delights in witnessing unceasing tortures; that He is regaled with the groans and shrieks and imprecations of the suffering creatures whom He holds in the flames of hell? Can these horrid sounds be music in the ear of Infinite Love? It is urged that the infliction of endless misery upon the wicked would show God's hatred of sin as an evil which is ruinous to the peace and order of the universe. Oh, dreadful blasphemy! As if God's hatred of sin is the reason why it is perpetuated. For, according to the teachings of these theologians, continued torture without hope of mercy maddens its wretched victims, and as they pour out their rage in curses and blasphemy, they are forever augmenting their load of guilt. God's glory is not enhanced by thus perpetuating continually increasing sin through ceaseless ages.

It is beyond the power of the human mind to estimate the evil which has been wrought by the heresy of eternal torment. The religion of the Bible, full of love and goodness, and abounding in compassion, is darkened by superstition and clothed with terror. When we consider in what false colors Satan has painted the character of God, can we wonder that our merciful Creator is feared, dreaded, and even hated? The appalling views of God which have spread over the world from the teachings of the pulpit have made thousands, yes, millions, of skeptics and infidels.

(14) WHAT IS THE DESCRIPTION GIVEN IN THIS VERSE THAT DESCRIBES FALSE DOCTRINE?

____

____

____

Revelation 14:8; 17:2

The theory of eternal torment is one of the false doctrines that constitute the wine of the abomination of Babylon, of which she makes all nations drink. Revelation 14:8; 17:2. That ministers of Christ should have accepted this heresy and proclaimed it from the sacred desk is indeed a mystery. . . . If we turn from the testimony of God's word, and accept false doctrines because our fathers taught them, we fall under the condemnation pronounced upon Babylon; we are drinking of the wine of her abomination.

(15) WHAT WILL THE LORD GIVE TO BOTH THE RIGHTEOUS AND THE SINNER?

Revelation 22:12

A large class to whom the doctrine of eternal torment is revolting are driven to the opposite error. They see that the Scriptures represent God as a being of love and compassion, and they cannot believe that He will consign His creatures to the fires of an eternally burning hell. But holding that the soul is naturally immortal, they see no alternative but to conclude that all mankind will finally be saved. Many regard the threatenings of the Bible as designed merely to frighten men into obedience, and not to be literally fulfilled. Thus the sinner can live in selfish pleasure, disregarding the requirements of God, and yet expect to be finally received into His favor. Such a doctrine, presuming upon God's mercy, but ignoring His justice, pleases the carnal heart and emboldens the wicked in their iniquity.

God has given in His word decisive evidence that He will punish the transgressors of His law. Those who flatter themselves that He is too merciful to execute justice upon the sinner, have only to look to the cross of Calvary. The death of the spotless Son of God testifies that "the wages of sin is death," that every violation of God's law must receive its just retribution. Christ the sinless became sin for man. He bore the guilt of transgression, and the hiding of His Father's face, until His heart was broken and His life crushed out. All this sacrifice was made that sinners might be redeemed. In no other way could man be freed from the penalty of sin. And every soul that refuses to become a partaker of the atonement provided at such a cost must bear in his own person the guilt and punishment of transgression.

(16) WHAT ESSENTIAL REQUIREMENTS MUST BE MET BEFORE SALVATION IS ASSURED?

Revelation 21:6

Revelation 21:7; Ephesians 5:5; Hebrews 12:14; Revelation 22:14,15

. . . This promise is only to those that thirst. None but those who feel their need of the water of life, and seek it at the loss of all things else, will be supplied. . . . In order to inherit all things, we must resist and overcome sin.

The Lord declares by the prophet Isaiah: "Say ye to the righteous, that it shall be well with him." "Woe unto the wicked! it shall be ill with him: for the reward of his hands shall be given him." Isaiah 3:10, 11. "Though a sinner do evil an hundred times," says the wise man, "and his days be prolonged, yet surely I know that it shall be well with them that fear God, which fear before Him: but it shall not be well with the wicked." Ecclesiastes 8:12, 13. And Paul testifies that the sinner is treasuring up unto himself "wrath against the day of wrath and revelation of the righteous judgment of God; who will render to every man according to his deeds;" "tribulation and anguish upon every soul of man that doeth evil." Romans 2:5, 6,9.

(17) HOW WILL GOD DEAL WITH REBELLION AND SIN?

Exodus 34:6,7

Psalms 145:20; 37:38

God has given to men a declaration of His character and of His method of dealing with sin. . . . The power and authority of the divine government will be employed to put down rebellion; yet all the manifestations of retributive justice will be perfectly consistent with the character of God as a merciful, long-suffering, benevolent being.

(18) WHAT IS GOD'S PLEA TO EVERY SINNER?

Isaiah 1:18; 2 Chronicles 7:14

God does not force the will or judgment of any. He takes no pleasure in a slavish obedience. He desires that the creatures of His hands shall love Him because He is worthy of love. He would have them obey Him because they have an intelligent appreciation of His wisdom, justice, and benevolence. And all who have a just conception of these qualities will love Him because they are drawn toward Him in admiration of His attributes.

The principles of kindness, mercy, and love, taught and exemplified by our Saviour, are a transcript of the will and character of God. Christ declared that He taught nothing except that which He had received from His Father. The principles of the divine government are in perfect harmony with the Saviour's precept, "Love your enemies." God executes justice upon the wicked, for the good of the universe, and even for the good of those upon whom His judgments are visited. He would make them happy if He could do so in accordance with the laws of His government and the justice of His character. He surrounds them with the tokens of His love, He grants them a knowledge of His law, and follows them with the offers of His mercy; but they despise His love, make void His law, and reject His mercy. While constantly receiving His gifts, they dishonor the Giver; they hate God because they know that He abhors their sins. The Lord bears long with their perversity; but the decisive hour will come at last, when their destiny is to be decided. Will He then chain these rebels to His side? Will He force them to do His will?

(19) WHAT CRY WILL COME FROM THE WICKED AS THEY EXPERIENCE THE PRESENCE OF THE LORD?

Revelation 6:16

Those who have chosen Satan as their leader and have been controlled by his power are not prepared to enter the presence of God. Pride, deception, licentiousness, cruelty, have become fixed in their characters. Can they enter heaven to dwell forever with those whom they despised and hated on earth?

Truth will never be agreeable to a liar; meekness will not satisfy self-esteem and pride; purity is not acceptable to the corrupt; disinterested love does not appear attractive to the selfish. What source of enjoyment could heaven offer to those who are wholly absorbed in earthly and selfish interests?

Could those whose lives have been spent in rebellion against God be suddenly transported to heaven and witness the high, the holy state of perfection that ever exists there,—every soul filled with love, every countenance beaming with joy, enrapturing music in melodious strains rising in honor of God and the Lamb, and ceaseless streams of light flowing upon the redeemed from the face of Him who sitteth upon the throne,—could those whose hearts are filled with hatred of God, of truth and holiness, mingle with the heavenly throng and join their songs of praise? Could they endure the glory of God and the Lamb? No, no; years of probation were granted them, that they might form characters for heaven; but they have never trained the mind to love purity; they have never learned the language of heaven, and now it is too late. A life of rebellion against God has unfitted them for heaven. Its purity, holiness, and peace would be torture to them; the glory of God would be a consuming fire. They would long to flee from that holy place. They would welcome destruction, that they might be hidden from the face of Him who died to redeem them. The destiny of the wicked is fixed by their own choice. Their exclusion from heaven is voluntary with themselves, and just and merciful on the part of God.

(20) WHAT PROCLAMATION FROM GOD WILL SEAL THE FATE OF ALL HUMANITY FOR ETERNITY?

____

____

____

____

____

Revelation 22:11

Like the waters of the Flood the fires of the great day declare God's verdict that the wicked are incurable. They have no disposition to submit to divine authority. Their will has been exercised in revolt; and when life is ended, it is too late to turn the current of their thoughts in the opposite direction, too late to turn from transgression to obedience, from hatred to love.

(21) WHAT WAS THE RESULT OF GOD SPARING CAIN FOLLOWING THE MURDER OF ABEL?

____

____

____

Genesis 6:5

In sparing the life of Cain the murderer, God gave the world an example of what would be the result of permitting the sinner to live to continue a course of unbridled iniquity. Through the influence of Cain's teaching and example, multitudes of his descendants were led into sin, until "the wickedness of man was great in the earth" and "every imagination of the thoughts of his heart was only evil continually." "The earth also was corrupt before God, and the earth was filled with violence." Genesis 6:5, 11.

In mercy to the world, God blotted out its wicked inhabitants in Noah's time. In mercy He destroyed the corrupt dwellers in Sodom. Through the deceptive power of Satan the workers of iniquity obtain sympathy and admiration, and are thus constantly leading others to rebellion. It was so in Cain's and in Noah's day, and in the time of Abraham and Lot; it is so in our time. It is in mercy to the universe that God will finally destroy the rejecters of His grace.

(22) HOW CAN THE SACRIFICE OF CHRIST REDEEM ALL REPENTANT SINNERS?

____

____

____

____

Romans 5:17-10; Acts 24:15

In consequence of Adam's sin, death passed upon the whole human race. All alike go down into the grave. And through the provisions of the plan of salvation, all are to be brought forth from their graves.

(23) WHAT DETERMINES THE MEASURE OF PUNISHMENT THE WICKED WILL RECEIVE?

____

____

Matthew 16:27

"There shall be a resurrection of the dead, both of the just and unjust;" 1 Cornthians 15:22 . . . But a distinction is made between the two classes that are brought forth. "All that are in the graves shall hear His voice, and shall come forth; they that have done good, unto the resurrection of life; and they that have done evil, unto the resurrection of damnation." John 5:28, 29. They who have been "accounted worthy" of the resurrection of life are "blessed and holy." "On such the second death hath no power." Revelation 20:6. But those who have not, through repentance and faith, secured pardon, must receive the penalty of transgression—"the wages of sin." They suffer punishment varying in duration and intensity, "according to their works," but finally ending in the second death. Since it is impossible for God, consistently with His justice and mercy, to save the sinner in his sins, He deprives him of the existence which his transgressions have forfeited and of which he has proved himself unworthy.

(24) WHAT IS THE FINAL STATE OF THE SOUL THAT SINS?

____

____

Romans 6:23

____

____

Obadiah 16; Psalm 37:10

Thus will be made an end of sin, with all the woe and ruin which have resulted from it. Says the psalmist: "Thou hast destroyed the wicked, Thou hast put out their name forever and ever. O thou enemy, destructions are come to a perpetual end." Psalm 9:5, 6. John, in the Revelation, looking forward to the eternal state, hears a universal anthem of praise undisturbed by one note of discord. Every creature in heaven and earth was heard ascribing glory to God. Revelation 5:13. There will then be no lost souls to blaspheme God as they writhe in never-ending torment; no wretched beings in hell will mingle their shrieks with the songs of the saved.

(25) WHAT IS THE CONDITION OF ALL THOSE WHO DIE?

____

____

Ecclesiastes 9:5

Upon the fundamental error of natural immortality rests the doctrine of consciousness in death—a doctrine, like eternal torment, opposed to the teachings of the Scriptures, to the dictates of reason, and to our feelings of humanity. According to the popular belief, the redeemed in heaven are acquainted with all that takes place on the earth and especially with the lives of the friends whom they have left behind. But how could it be a source of happiness to the dead to know the troubles of the living, to witness the sins committed by their own loved ones, and to see them enduring all the sorrows, disappointments, and anguish of life? How much of heaven's bliss would be enjoyed by those who were hovering over their friends on earth? And how utterly revolting is the belief that as soon as the breath leaves the body the soul of the impenitent is consigned to the flames of hell! To what depths of anguish must those be plunged who see their friends passing to the grave unprepared, to enter upon an eternity of woe and sin! Many have been driven to insanity by this harrowing thought.

What say the Scriptures concerning these things? David declares that man is not conscious in death. "His breath goeth forth, he returneth to his earth; in that very day his thoughts perish." Psalm 146:4.

(26) WHAT CAN THE LIVING DO THAT THE DEAD CANNOT?

Isaiah 38:18,19

When, in answer to his prayer, Hezekiah's life was prolonged fifteen years, the grateful king rendered to God a tribute of praise for His great mercy. In this song he tells the reason why he thus rejoices: "The grave cannot praise Thee, death cannot celebrate Thee: they that go down into the pit cannot hope for Thy truth. The living, the living, he shall praise Thee, as I do this day." Isaiah 38:18, 19. Popular theology represents the righteous dead as in heaven, entered into bliss and praising God with an immortal tongue; but Hezekiah could see no such glorious prospect in death. With his words agrees the testimony of the psalmist: "In death there is no remembrance of Thee: in the grave who shall give Thee thanks?" "The dead praise not the Lord, neither any that go down into silence." Psalms 6:5; 115:17.

(27) WHERE IS KING DAVID TODAY?

Acts 2:29

The fact that David remains in the grave until the resurrection proves that the righteous do not go to heaven at death. It is only through the resurrection, and by virtue of the fact that Christ has risen, that David can at last sit at the right hand of God.

(28) FROM WHERE WILL THE DEAD COME ON RESURRECTION DAY?

____

____

John 5:28,29

(29) WHY IS IT NOT LOGICAL FOR THOSE WHO HAVE DIED TO GO TO HEAVEN OR HELL BEFORE THE DAY CHRIST RETURNS?

____

____

____

____

Revelation 22:12

And said Paul: "If the dead rise not, then is not Christ raised: and if Christ be not raised, your faith is vain; ye are yet in your sins. Then they also which are fallen asleep in Christ are perished." I Corinthians 15:16-18. If for four thousand years the righteous had gone directly to heaven at death, how could Paul have said that if there is no resurrection, "they also which are fallen asleep in Christ are perished"? No resurrection would be necessary.

(30) AT CHRIST'S ASCENSION, WHAT PRECIOUS PROMISE DID HE LEAVE FOR THOSE WHO WOULD LONG FOR HIS RETURN?

____

____

____

____

____

____

John 14:2,3

But when about to leave His disciples, Jesus did not tell them that they would soon come to Him. . . . And Paul tells us, further, that "the Lord Himself shall descend from heaven with a shout, with the voice of the Archangel, and with the trump of God: and the dead in Christ shall rise first: then we which are alive and remain shall be caught up together with them in the clouds, to meet the Lord in the air: and so shall we ever be with the Lord." And he adds: "Comfort one another with these words." I Thessalonians 4:16-18. . . . Paul points his brethren to the future coming of the Lord, when the fetters of the tomb shall be broken, and the "dead in Christ" shall be raised to eternal life.

(31) WHAT GREAT AND SOLEMN EVENT MUST TAKE PLACE BEFORE THE RIGHTEOUS AND THE WICKED RECEIVE THEIR REWARDS?

____

____

____

Revelation 20:12

Before any can enter the mansions of the blessed, their cases must be investigated, and their characters and their deeds must pass in review before God. All are to be judged according to the things written in the books and to be rewarded as their works have been. This judgment does not take place at death. Mark the words of Paul: "He hath appointed a day, in the which He will judge the world in righteousness by that Man whom He hath ordained; whereof He hath given assurance unto all men, in that He hath raised Him from the dead." Acts 17:31. Here the apostle plainly stated that a specified time, then future, had been fixed upon for the judgment of the world.

Jude refers to the same period: "The angels which kept not their first estate, but left their own habitation, He hath reserved in everlasting chains under darkness unto the judgment of the great day." And, again, he quotes the words of Enoch: "Behold, the Lord cometh with ten thousands of His saints, to execute judgment upon all." Jude 6, 14, 15. . . .

But if the dead are already enjoying the bliss of heaven or writhing in the flames of hell, what need of a future judgment? The teachings of God's word on these important points are neither obscure nor contradictory; they may be understood by common minds. But what candid mind can see either wisdom or justice in the current theory? Will the righteous, after the investigation of their cases at the judgment, receive the commendation, "Well done, thou good and faithful servant: . . . enter thou into the joy of thy Lord," when they have been dwelling in His presence, perhaps for long ages? Are the wicked summoned from the place of torment to receive sentence from the Judge of all the earth: "Depart from Me, ye cursed, into everlasting fire"? Matthew 25:21, 41. Oh, solemn mockery! shameful impeachment of the wisdom and justice of God!

(32) IN WHAT STATE DO THE DEAD REMAIN UNTIL THE RESURRECTION?

____

____

____

____

Daniel 12:2; Psalm 13:3; Job 7:21

Nowhere in the Sacred Scriptures is found the statement that the righteous go to their reward or the wicked to their punishment at death. The patriarchs and prophets have left no such assurance. Christ and His apostles have given no hint of it. The Bible clearly teaches that the dead do not go immediately to heaven. They are represented as sleeping until the resurrection. I Thessalonians 4:14; Job 14:10-12. In the very day when the silver cord is loosed and the golden bowl broken (Ecclesiastes 12:6), man's thoughts perish. They that go down to the grave are in silence. They know no more of anything that is done under the sun. Job 14:21. Blessed rest for the weary righteous! Time, be it long or short, is but a moment to them. They sleep; they are awakened by the trump of God to a glorious immortality. "For the trumpet shall sound, and the dead shall be raised incorruptible. . . .So when this corruptible shall have put on incorruption, and this mortal shall have put on immortality, then shall be brought to pass the saying that is written, Death is swallowed up in victory." I Corinthians 15:52-54.

(33) WHAT WILL BE THE VICTORY CRY OF THE RESURRECTED RIGHTEOUS?

____

____

____

____

1 Corinthians 15:55

As they are called forth from their deep slumber they begin to think just where they ceased. The last sensation was the pang of death; the last thought, that they were falling beneath the power of the grave. When they arise from the tomb, their first glad thought will be echoed in the triumphal shout: "O death, where is thy sting? O grave, where is thy victory?"

I realize that the first deception to mankind was, "Ye shall not surely die." It is clear that the Bible teaches that the ultimate result of unrepented sin brings final death to both the body and soul.

Circle: Yes Undecided

I have discovered in God's Word that our only hope for immortality is to accept the atoning sacrifice of Christ.

Circle: Yes Undecided

I see the evidence of the great controversy and Satan's effort is to convince the world that God's government is stern and unfair. But, it is evident in Scripture that all God's judgements are righteous, just, and merciful.

Circle: Yes Undecided

I see God's mercy in the fact that after receiving their just reward, the wicked will be destroyed in the fires of hell. Neither their body or soul will be left to suffer for endless ages.

Circle: Yes Undecided

I have found in Scripture that the dead are not in heaven praising God. They have no emotion, thought, or any awareness of any kind but are asleep in their graves awaiting the resurrection.

Circle: Yes Undecided

It gives me peace to know they are not observing their loved ones suffering the injustices of this world. They are asleep in their grave awaiting the resurrection at the second coming of Christ.

Circle: Yes Undecided

It is my prayer that I will be among those faithful followers who cry out, "O death, where is thy sting? O grave, where is they victory?".

Circle: Yes Undecided

Study Notes: ____________________

____

____

____

____

____

____

____

Can The Dead Speak to Us? - 6

The ministration of holy angels, as presented in the Scriptures, is a truth most comforting and precious to every follower of Christ. But the Bible teaching upon this point has been obscured and perverted by the errors of popular theology. The doctrine of natural immortality, first borrowed from the pagan philosophy, and in the darkness of the great apostasy incorporated into the Christian faith, has supplanted the truth, so plainly taught in Scripture, that "the dead know not anything." Multitudes have come to believe that it is spirits of the dead who are the "ministering spirits, sent forth to minister for them who shall be heirs of salvation." And this notwithstanding the testimony of Scripture to the existence of heavenly angels, and their connection with the history of man, before the death of a human being.

(1) WHAT WILL THE DEAD NOT DO AFTER ENTERING THE GRAVE?

____

____

____

Job 7:9

The doctrine of man's consciousness in death, especially the belief that spirits of the dead return to minister to the living, has prepared the way for modern spiritualism. If the dead are admitted to the presence of God and holy angels, and privileged with knowledge far exceeding what they before possessed, why should they not return to the earth to enlighten and instruct the living? If, as taught by popular theologians, spirits of the dead are hovering about their friends on earth, why should they not be permitted to communicate with them, to warn them against evil, or to comfort them in sorrow? How can those who believe in man's consciousness in death reject what comes to them as divine light communicated by glorified spirits? Here is a channel regarded as sacred, through which Satan works for the accomplishment of his purposes. The fallen angels who do his bidding appear as messengers from the spirit world. While professing to bring the living into communication with the dead, the prince of evil exercises his bewitching influence upon their minds.

(2) WHAT ABILITY DO THE FORCES OF EVIL POSSESS AND USE IN AN ATTEMPT TO DECEIVE THE WORLD?

____

____

____

Matthew 24:24; Revelation 16:14

He has power to bring before men the appearance of their departed friends. The counterfeit is perfect; the familiar look, the words, the tone, are reproduced with marvelous distinctness. Many are comforted with the assurance that their loved ones are enjoying the bliss of heaven, and without suspicion of danger, they give ear "to seducing spirits, and doctrines of devils." When they have been led to believe that the dead actually return to communicate with them, Satan causes those to appear who went into the grave unprepared. They claim to be happy in heaven and even to occupy exalted positions there, and thus the error is widely taught that no difference is made between the righteous and the wicked. The pretended visitants from the world of spirits sometimes utter cautions and warnings which prove to be correct. Then, as confidence is gained, they present doctrines that directly undermine faith in the Scriptures. With an appearance of deep interest in the well-being of their friends on earth, they insinuate the most dangerous errors. The fact that they state some truths, and are able at times to foretell future events, gives to their statements an appearance of reliability; and their false teachings are accepted by the multitudes as readily, and believed as implicitly, as if they were the most sacred truths of the Bible. The law of God is set aside, the Spirit of grace despised, the blood of the covenant counted an unholy thing. The spirits deny the deity of Christ and place even the Creator on a level with themselves. Thus under a new disguise the great rebel still carries on his warfare against God, begun in heaven and for nearly six thousand years continued upon the earth.

(3) IN THIS BIBLICAL EXAMPLE, WHO WAS IT THAT THE SPIRITS OF EVIL IMPERSONATED?

____

____

1 Samuel 28:14

Many endeavor to account for spiritual manifestations by attributing them wholly to fraud and sleight of hand on the part of the medium. But while it is true that the results of trickery have often been palmed off as genuine manifestations, there have been, also, marked exhibitions of supernatural power. The mysterious rapping with which modern spiritualism began was not the result of human trickery or cunning, but was the direct work of evil angels, who thus introduced one of the most successful of soul-destroying delusions. Many will be ensnared through the belief that spiritualism is a merely human imposture; when brought face to face with manifestations which they cannot but regard as supernatural, they will be deceived, and will be led to accept them as the great power of God.

(4) WHAT THREE CATEGORIES DESCRIBE THE MANIFESTATION OF SATANIC POWERS?

____

____

____

2 Thessalonians 2:9,10

These persons overlook the testimony of the Scriptures concerning the wonders wrought by Satan and his agents. It was by satanic aid that Pharaoh's magicians were enabled to counterfeit the work of God. Paul testifies that before the second advent of Christ there will be similar manifestations of satanic power. . . . And the apostle John, describing the miracle-working power that will be manifested in the last days, declares: "He doeth great wonders, so that he maketh fire come down from heaven on the earth in the sight of men, and deceiveth them that dwell on the earth by the means of those miracles which he had power to do." Revelation 13:13,14. No mere impostures are here foretold. Men are deceived by the miracles which Satan's agents have power to do, not which they pretend to do.

(5) WHAT WILL BE SATAN'S MASTERPIECE OF DECEPTION?

____

____

____

2 Corinthians 11:13,14

The prince of darkness, who has so long bent the powers of his mastermind to the work of deception, skillfully adapts his temptations to men of all classes and conditions. To persons of culture and refinement he presents spiritualism in its more refined and intellectual aspects, and thus succeeds in drawing many into his snare. The wisdom which spiritualism imparts is that described by the apostle James, which "descendeth not from above, but is earthly, sensual, devilish." James 3:15. This, however, the great deceiver conceals when concealment will best suit his purpose. He who could appear clothed with the brightness of the heavenly seraphs before Christ in the wilderness of temptation, comes to men in the most attractive manner as an angel of light. He appeals to the reason by the presentation of elevating themes; he delights the fancy with enrapturing scenes; and he enlists the affections by his eloquent portrayals of love and charity. He excites the imagination to lofty flights, leading men to take so great pride in their own wisdom that in their hearts they despise the Eternal One. That mighty being who could take the world's Redeemer to an exceedingly high mountain and bring before Him all the kingdoms of the earth and the glory of them, will present his temptations to men in a manner to pervert the senses of all who are not shielded by divine power.

(6) WHAT IS THE SOURCE OF FORBIDDEN KNOWLEDGE AND SELF-EXALTATION THAT EVIL MEN DESIRE?

____

____

James 3:15

Satan beguiles men now as he beguiled Eve in Eden by flattery, by kindling a desire to obtain forbidden knowledge, by exciting ambition for self-exaltation. It was cherishing these evils that caused his fall, and through them he aims to compass the ruin of men. "Ye shall be as gods," he declares, "knowing good and evil." Genesis 3:5. Spiritualism teaches "that man is the creature of progression; that it is his destiny from his birth to progress, even to eternity, toward the Godhead." . . .

Thus, in place of the righteousness and perfection of the infinite God, the true object of adoration; in place of the perfect righteousness of His law, the true standard of human attainment, Satan has substituted the sinful, erring nature of man himself as the only object of adoration, the only rule of judgment, or standard of character. This is progress, not upward, but downward.

(7) HOW ONLY CAN MANKIND BE EXALTED?

____

____

____

James 4:6; Matthew 23:12

It is a law both of the intellectual and the spiritual nature that by beholding we become changed. The mind gradually adapts itself to the subjects upon which it is allowed to dwell. It becomes assimilated to that which it is accustomed to love and reverence. Man will never rise higher than his standard of purity or goodness or truth. If self is his loftiest ideal, he will never attain to anything more exalted. Rather, he will constantly sink lower and lower. The grace of God alone has power to exalt man. Left to himself, his course must inevitably be downward.

(8) WHAT IS MAN'S PART IN COOPERATION WITH GOD AGAINST SELF-INDULGENCE?

____

____

____

1 Corinthians 9:25

To the self-indulgent, the pleasure-loving, the sensual, spiritualism presents itself under a less subtle disguise than to the more refined and intellectual; in its grosser forms they find that which is in harmony with their inclinations. Satan studies every indication of the frailty of human nature, he marks the sins which each individual is inclined to commit, and then he takes care that opportunities shall not be wanting to gratify the tendency to evil. He tempts men to excess in that which is in itself lawful, causing them, through intemperance, to weaken physical, mental, and moral power. He has destroyed and is destroying thousands through the indulgence of the passions, thus brutalizing the entire nature of man. And to complete his work, he declares, through the spirits that "true knowledge places man above all law;" that "whatever is, is right;" that "God doth not condemn;" and that "all sins which are committed are innocent." When the people are thus led to believe that desire is the highest law, that liberty is license, and that man is accountable only to himself, who can wonder that corruption and depravity teem on every hand? Multitudes eagerly accept teachings that leave them at liberty to obey the promptings of the carnal heart. The reins of self-control are laid upon the neck of lust, the powers of mind and soul are made subject to the animal propensities, and Satan exultingly sweeps into his net thousands who profess to be followers of Christ.

(9) WHAT WARNING DOES SCRIPTURE GIVE REGARDING INVOLVEMENT IN SPIRITUALISM?

____

____

____

____

Leviticus 19:31; Isaiah 8:20

But none need be deceived by the lying claims of spiritualism. God has given the world sufficient light to enable them to discover the snare. As already shown, the theory which forms the very foundation of spiritualism is at war with the plainest statements of Scripture. The Bible declares that the dead know not anything, that their thoughts have perished; they have no part in anything that is done under the sun; they know nothing of the joys or sorrows of those who were dearest to them on earth.

(10) TO REVEAL THE SERIOUSNESS OF THE ISSUE OF SPIRITUALISM, WHAT PENALTY DID GOD DECREE TO THOSE WHO BECAME INVOLVED?

____

____

____

Leviticus 20:27; 19:31

Furthermore, God has expressly forbidden all pretended communication with departed spirits. In the days of the Hebrews there was a class of people who claimed, as do the spiritualists of today, to hold communication with the dead. But the "familiar spirits," as these visitants from other worlds were called, are declared by the Bible to be "the spirits of devils." (Compare Numbers 25:1-3; Psalm 106:28; I Corinthians 10:20; Revelation 16:14.) The work of dealing with familiar spirits was pronounced an abomination to the Lord, and was solemnly forbidden under penalty of death. The very name of witchcraft is now held in contempt. The claim that men can hold intercourse with evil spirits is regarded as a fable of the Dark Ages. But spiritualism, which numbers its converts by hundreds of thousands, yea, by millions, which has made its way into scientific circles, which has invaded churches, and has found favor in legislative bodies, and even in the courts of kings—this mammoth deception is but a revival, in a new disguise, of the witchcraft condemned and prohibited of old.

If there were no other evidence of the real character of spiritualism, it should be enough for the Christian that the spirits make no difference between righteousness and sin, between the noblest and purest of the apostles of Christ and the most corrupt of the servants of Satan. By representing the basest of men as in heaven, and highly exalted there, Satan says to the world: "No matter how wicked you are; no matter whether you believe or disbelieve God and the Bible. Live as you please; heaven is your home." The spiritualist teachers virtually declare: "Everyone that doeth evil is good in the sight of the Lord, and He delighteth in them; or, Where is the God of judgment?" Malachi 2:17. Saith the word of God: "Woe unto them that call evil good, and good evil; that put darkness for light, and light for darkness." Isaiah 5:20.

(11) WHY IS THE BIBLE THE ONLY RELIABLE SOURCE OF COUNSEL REGARDING SPIRITUALISM?

John 17:17

The apostles, as personated by these lying spirits, are made to contradict what they wrote at the dictation of the Holy Spirit when on earth. They deny the divine origin of the Bible, and thus tear away the foundation of the Christian's hope and put out the light that reveals the way to heaven. Satan is making the world believe that the Bible is a mere fiction, or at least a book suited to the infancy of the race, but now to be lightly regarded, or cast aside as obsolete. And to take the place of the word of God he holds our spiritual manifestations. Here is a channel wholly under his control; by this means he can make the world believe what he will. The Book that is to judge him and his followers he puts in the shade, just where he wants it; the Saviour of the world he makes to be no more than a common man. And as the Roman guard that watched the tomb of Jesus spread the lying report which the priests and elders put into their mouths to disprove His resurrection, so do the believers in spiritual manifestations try to make it appear that there is nothing miraculous in the circumstances of our Saviour's life. After thus seeking to put Jesus in the background, they call attention to their own miracles, declaring that these far exceed the works of Christ.

(12) WHAT SOURCE OF POWER DOES SPIRITUALISM CLAIM?

Acts 8:9,10

It is true that spiritualism is now changing its form and, veiling some of its more objectionable features, is assuming a Christian guise. But its utterances from the platform and the press have been before the public for many years, and in these its real character stands revealed. These teachings cannot be denied or hidden.

Even in its present form, so far from being more worthy of toleration than formerly, it is really a more dangerous, because a more subtle, deception. While it formerly denounced Christ and the Bible, it now professes to accept both. But the Bible is interpreted in a manner that is pleasing to the unrenewed heart, while its solemn and vital truths are made of no effect. Love is dwelt upon as the chief attribute of God, but it is degraded to a weak sentimentalism, making little distinction between good and evil. God's justice, His denunciations of sin, the requirements of His holy law, are all kept out of sight. The people are taught to regard the Decalogue as a dead letter. Pleasing, bewitching fables captivate the senses and lead men to reject the Bible as the foundation of their faith. Christ is as verily denied as before; but Satan has so blinded the eyes of the people that the deception is not discerned.

(13) WHAT DIRECTIVE DOES SCRIPTURE GIVE TO SAFEGUARD US FROM DECEPTION?

---

2 Timothy 2:15

There are few who have any just conception of the deceptive power of spiritualism and the danger of coming under its influence. Many tamper with it merely to gratify their curiosity. They have no real faith in it and would be filled with horror at the thought of yielding themselves to the spirits' control. But they venture upon the forbidden ground, and the mighty destroyer exercises his power upon them against their will. Let them once be induced to submit their minds to his direction, and he holds them captive. It is impossible, in their own strength, to break away from the bewitching, alluring spell. Nothing but the power of God, granted in answer to the earnest prayer of faith, can deliver these ensnared souls.

(14) WHAT IS THE RESULT OF INDULGENCE IN ANY KNOWN SIN?

____

____

Isaiah 59:2

All who indulge sinful traits of character, or willfully cherish a known sin, are inviting the temptations of Satan. They separate themselves from God and from the watchcare of His angels; as the evil one presents his deceptions, they are without defense and fall an easy prey. Those who thus place themselves in his power little realize where their course will end. Having achieved their overthrow, the tempter will employ them as his agents to lure others to ruin.

(15) WHY WILL MANY BELIEVE "STRONG DELUSIONS"?

____

____

____

2 Thessalonians 2:10,11

Says the prophet Isaiah: "When they shall say unto you, Seek unto them that have familiar spirits, and unto wizards that peep, and that mutter: should not a people seek unto their God? for the living to the dead? To the law and to the testimony: if they speak not according to this word, it is because there is no light in them." Isaiah 8:19, 20. If men had been willing to receive the truth so plainly stated in the Scriptures concerning the nature of man and the state of the dead, they would see in the claims and manifestations of spiritualism the working of Satan with power and signs and lying wonders. But rather than yield the liberty so agreeable to the carnal heart, and renounce the sins which they love, multitudes close their eyes to the light and walk straight on, regardless of warnings, while Satan weaves his snares about them, and they become his prey. "Because they received not the love of the truth, that they might be saved," therefore "God shall send them strong delusion, that they should believe a lie."

(16) WHEN WE STAND ON THE TRUTH OF GOD'S WORD WHO ARE WE OPPOSING?

____

____

Romans 8:38

Those who oppose the teachings of spiritualism are assailing, not men alone, but Satan and his angels. They have entered upon a contest against principalities and powers and wicked spirits in high places. Satan will not yield one inch of ground except as he is driven back by the power of heavenly messengers. The people of God should be able to meet him, as did our Saviour, with the words: "It is written." Satan can quote Scripture now as in the days of Christ, and he will pervert its teachings to sustain his delusions. Those who would stand in this time of peril must understand for themselves the testimony of the Scriptures.

(17) IF CONFRONTED BY EVIL SPIRITS IMPERSONATING THE DEAD, WHAT TRUTH WILL PROTECT US FROM DECEPTION?

____

____

Ecclesiastes 9:5

Many will be confronted by the spirits of devils personating beloved relatives or friends and declaring the most dangerous heresies. These visitants will appeal to our tenderest sympathies and will work miracles to sustain their pretensions. We must be prepared to withstand them with the Bible truth that the dead know not anything and that they who thus appear are the spirits of devils.

(18) IF WE FOLLOWED GOD'S WORD, WHAT GREAT PROMISE MAY WE CLAIM DURING OUR "HOUR OF TEMPTATION"?

____

____

____

Revelation 3:10

Just before us is "the hour of temptation, which shall come upon all the world, to try them that dwell upon the earth." All whose faith is not firmly established upon the word of God will be deceived and overcome. Satan "works with all deceivableness of unrighteousness" to gain control of the children of men, and his deceptions will continually increase. But he can gain his object only as men voluntarily yield to his temptations. Those who are earnestly seeking a knowledge of the truth and are striving to purify their souls through obedience, thus doing what they can to prepare for the conflict, will find, in the God of truth, a sure defense. "Because thou hast kept the word of My patience, I also will keep thee", is the Saviour's promise. He would sooner send every angel out of heaven to protect His people than leave one soul that trusts in Him to be overcome by Satan.

(19) WHAT DANGER RESTS IN BLIND ACCEPTANCE OF COMMON BELIEFS WITHOUT SEARCHING FOR AND ACCEPTING TRUTH FOR OURSELVES?

____

____

Hosea 4:6

The prophet Isaiah brings to view the fearful deception which will come upon the wicked, causing them to count themselves secure from the judgments of God: "We have made a covenant with death, and with hell are we at agreement; when the overflowing scourge shall pass through, it shall not come unto us: for we have made lies our refuge, and under falsehood have we hid ourselves." Isaiah 28:15. In the class here described are included those who in their stubborn impenitence comfort themselves with the assurance that there is to be no punishment for the sinner; that all mankind, it matters not how corrupt, are to be exalted to heaven, to become as the angels of God. But still more emphatically are those making a covenant with death and an agreement with hell, who renounce the truths which Heaven has provided as a defense for the righteous in the day of trouble, and accept the refuge of lies offered by Satan in its stead—the delusive pretensions of spiritualism.

(20) WHAT LIE TOLD IN THE GARDEN BY SATAN IS THE BASIS FOR ALL SPIRITUALISM?

____

____

____

____

Genesis 3:4

Satan has long been preparing for his final effort to deceive the world. The foundation of his work was laid by the assurance given to Eve in Eden: "Ye shall not surely die." "In the day ye eat thereof, then your eyes shall be opened, and ye shall be as gods, knowing good and evil." Little by little he has prepared the way for his masterpiece of deception in the development of spiritualism. He has not yet reached the full accomplishment of his designs; but it will be reached in the last remnant of time. Says the prophet: "I saw three unclean spirits like frogs; . . . they are the spirits of devils, working miracles, which go forth unto the kings of the earth and of the whole world, to gather them to the battle of that great day of God Almighty." Revelation 16:13,14. Except those who are kept by the power of God, through faith in His word, the whole world will be swept into the ranks of this delusion. The people are fast being lulled to a fatal security, to be awakened only by the outpouring of the wrath of God.

(21) WHEN THIS GREAT CONTROVERSY CLOSES WHAT WILL BECOME OF SATAN'S "REFUGE OF LIES"?

____

____

____

____

Isaiah 28:17

By my study I am aware that in the last days the prince of evil will attempt to exert his bewitching influence upon our minds professing that communication exists between the living and the dead.

Circle: Yes Undecided

I am grateful to God for exposing Satan's two major deceptions – immortality of the soul, and conscienciousness in death, so that by His Word I won't be deceived.

Circle: Yes Undecided

I see the importance of the study of God's Word. I claim God's promise to reveal truth to me as I seek it so that I won't fall prey to Satan's deceptions.

Circle: Yes Undecided

I realize the Bible warns us of the perilous times we will face at the end of earth's history and I am so thankful for the promise that if I keep His Word He will keep me. By His power I will receive the promise of eternal life.

Circle: Yes Undecided

The Impending Conflict - 7

(1) WHAT IS THE IMPLICATION OF BREAKING EVEN ONE OF GOD'S LAWS?

____

____

____

James 2:10

From the very beginning of the great controversy in heaven it has been Satan's purpose to overthrow the law of God. It was to accomplish this that he entered upon his rebellion against the Creator, and though he was cast out of heaven he has continued the same warfare upon the earth. To deceive men, and thus lead them to transgress God's law, is the object which he has steadfastly pursued. Whether this be accomplished by casting aside the law altogether, or by rejecting one of its precepts, the result will be ultimately the same. He that offends "in one point," manifests contempt for the whole law; his influence and example are on the side of transgression; he becomes "guilty of all."

(2) WHAT IS SATAN'S PURPOSE IN THE DEGRADATION OF GOD'S LAWS?

____

____

____

***Romans** 7:7;* Romans 3:20

In seeking to cast contempt upon the divine statutes, Satan has perverted the doctrines of the Bible, and errors have thus become incorporated into the faith of thousands who profess to believe the Scriptures. The last great conflict between truth and error is but the final struggle of the long-standing controversy concerning the law of God. Upon this battle we are now entering—a battle between the laws of men and the precepts of Jehovah, between the religion of the Bible and the religion of fable and tradition.

(3) WHAT IS THE PURPOSE OF GOD'S WORD AND THE LAW IT CONTAINS?

____

____

____

Psalm 119:105

The agencies which will unite against truth and righteousness in this contest are now actively at work. God's holy word, which has been handed down to us at such a cost of suffering and blood, is but little valued. The Bible is within the reach of all, but there are few who really accept it as the guide of life.

(4) WHAT IS THE ROOT CAUSE OF INFIDELITY?

____

____

____

Jeremiah 8:9

Infidelity prevails to an alarming extent, not in the world merely, but in the church. Many have come to deny doctrines which are the very pillars of the Christian faith. The great facts of creation as presented by the inspired writers, the fall of man, the atonement, and the perpetuity of the law of God, are practically rejected, either wholly or in part, by a large share of the professedly Christian world. Thousands who pride themselves upon their wisdom and independence regard it as an evidence of weakness to place implicit confidence in the Bible; they think it a proof of superior talent and learning to cavil at the Scriptures and to spiritualize and explain away their most important truths. Many ministers are teaching their people, and many professors and teachers are instructing their students, that the law of God has been changed or abrogated; and those who regard its requirements as still valid, to be literally obeyed, are thought to be deserving only of ridicule or contempt.

(5) WHAT DANGER LIES IN THE REJECTION OF TRUTH?

____

____

____

John 18:37

In rejecting the truth, men reject its Author. In trampling upon the law of God, they deny the authority of the Lawgiver. It is as easy to make an idol of false doctrines and theories as to fashion an idol of wood or stone. By misrepresenting the attributes of God, Satan leads men to conceive of Him in a false character. With many, a philosophical idol is enthroned in the place of Jehovah; while the living God, as He is revealed in His word, in Christ, and in the works of creation, is worshiped by but few. Thousands deify nature while they deny the God of nature. Though in a different form, idolatry exists in the Christian world today as verily as it existed among ancient Israel in the days of Elijah. The god of many professedly wise men, of philosophers, poets, politicians, journalists—the god of polished fashionable circles, of many colleges and universities, even of some theological institutions—is little better than Baal, the sun-god of Phoenicia.

(6) HOW LONG WILL THE LAW OF GOD REMAIN IN EFFECT?

____

____

____

Psalm 119:160

No error accepted by the Christian world strikes more boldly against the authority of Heaven, none is more directly opposed to the dictates of reason, none is more pernicious in its results, than the modern doctrine, so rapidly gaining ground, that God's law is no longer binding upon men. Every nation has its laws, which command respect and obedience; no government could exist without them; and can it be conceived that the Creator of the heavens and the earth has no law to govern the beings He has made? Suppose that prominent ministers were publicly to teach that the statutes which govern their land and protect the rights of its citizens were not obligatory—that they restricted the liberties of the people, and therefore ought not to be obeyed; how long would such men be tolerated in the pulpit? But is it a graver offense to disregard the laws of states and nations than to trample upon those divine precepts which are the foundation of all government?

(7) WHAT IS LAWLESSNESS?

____

____

____

1 John 3:4

It would be far more consistent for nations to abolish their statutes, and permit the people to do as they please, than for the Ruler of the universe to annul His law, and leave the world without a standard to condemn the guilty or justify the obedient. Would we know the result of making void the law of God? The experiment has been tried. Terrible were the scenes enacted in France when atheism became the controlling power. It was then demonstrated to the world that to throw off the restraints which God has imposed is to accept the rule of the cruelest of tyrants. When the standard of righteousness is set aside, the way is open for the prince of evil to establish his power in the earth.

Wherever the divine precepts are rejected, sin ceases to appear sinful or righteousness desirable. Those who refuse to submit to the government of God are wholly unfitted to govern themselves. Through their pernicious teachings the spirit of insubordination is implanted in the hearts of children and youth, who are naturally impatient of control; and a lawless, licentious state of society results. While scoffing at the credulity of those who obey the requirements of God, the multitudes eagerly accept the delusions of Satan. They give the rein to lust and practice the sins which have called down judgments upon the heathen.

(8) WHAT BIBLICAL PRINCIPLE WILL RESULT WHEN GOD'S LAWS ARE SET ASIDE?

____

____

Galations 6:7

Those who teach the people to regard lightly the commandments of God sow disobedience to reap disobedience. Let the restraint imposed by the divine law be wholly cast aside, and human laws would soon be disregarded. Because God forbids dishonest practices, coveting, lying, and defrauding, men are ready to trample upon His statutes as a hindrance to their worldly prosperity; but the results of banishing these precepts would be such as they do not anticipate. If the law were not binding, why should any fear to transgress? Property would no longer be safe. Men would obtain their neighbor's possessions by violence, and the strongest would become richest. Life itself would not be respected. The marriage vow would no longer stand as a sacred bulwark to protect the family. He who had the power, would, if he desired, take his neighbor's wife by violence. The fifth commandment would be set aside with the fourth. Children would not shrink from taking the life of their parents if by so doing they could obtain the desire of their corrupt hearts. The civilized world would become a horde of robbers and assassins; and peace, rest, and happiness would be banished from the earth.

(9) WHAT BLESSING IS LOST BY DISOBEDIENCE TO GOD'S COMMANDMENTS?

____

____

____

Proverbs 3:1,2; Revelation 22:14

Already the doctrine that men are released from obedience to God's requirements has weakened the force of moral obligation and opened the floodgates of iniquity upon the world. Lawlessness, dissipation, and corruption are sweeping in upon us like an overwhelming tide. In the family, Satan is at work. His banner waves, even in professedly Christian households. There is envy, evil surmising, hypocrisy, estrangement, emulation, strife, betrayal of sacred trusts, indulgence of lust. The whole system of religious principles and doctrines, which should form the foundation and framework of social life, seems to be a tottering mass, ready to fall to ruin. . .

(10) WHAT IS THE RESULT WHEN LAWLESSNESS CONTROLS THOSE WHO GOVERN THE PEOPLE?

____

____

____

____

Isaiah 59:13,14; Proverbs 28:15

Courts of justice are corrupt. Rulers are actuated by desire for gain and love of sensual pleasure. Intemperance has beclouded the faculties of many so that Satan has almost complete control of them. Jurists are perverted, bribed, deluded. Drunkenness and revelry, passion, envy, dishonesty of every sort, are represented among those who administer the laws. "Justice standeth afar off: for truth is fallen in the street, and equity cannot enter."

(11) WHAT IS THE RESULT WHEN FAITH IN GOD'S WORD IS LOST?

____

____

____

Psalm 119:70

The iniquity and spiritual darkness that prevailed under the supremacy of Rome were the inevitable result of her suppression of the Scriptures; but where is to be found the cause of the widespread infidelity, the rejection of the law of God, and the consequent corruption, under the full blaze of gospel light in an age of religious freedom? Now that Satan can no longer keep the world under his control by withholding the Scriptures, he resorts to other means to accomplish the same object. To destroy faith in the Bible serves his purpose as well as to destroy the Bible itself. By introducing the belief that God's law is not binding, he as effectually leads men to transgress as if they were wholly ignorant of its precepts. And now, as in former ages, he has worked through the church to further his designs. The religious organizations of the day have refused to listen to unpopular truths plainly brought to view in the Scriptures, and in combating them they have adopted interpretations and taken positions which have sown and broadcast the seeds of skepticism . . .

(12) WHAT DIVINE PROMISE IS GIVEN CONCERNING THE STABILITY OF GOD'S LAW?

____

____

Psalm 119:160; Matthew 5:17

(13) WHAT WILL BE THE FOREMOST CHARACTERISTIC OF THOSE WHO LOVE GOD AND ARE HIS LAST DAY REMNANT PEOPLE?

____

____

____

Revelation 14:12; 12:17

(14) THOUGH NEGLECTED BY THE MAJORITY, WHAT DAY HAS GOD ASKED US TO OBSERVE AS HIS SABBATH?

____

____

Exodus 20:8-11; Mark 2:27

And as the claims of the fourth commandment are urged upon the people, it is found that the observance of the seventh-day Sabbath is enjoined; and as the only way to free themselves from a duty which they are unwilling to perform, many popular teachers declare that the law of God is no longer binding. Thus they cast away the law and the Sabbath together. As the work of Sabbath reform extends, this rejection of the divine law to avoid the claims of the fourth commandment will become well-nigh universal. The teachings of religious leaders have opened the door to infidelity, to spiritualism, and to contempt for God's holy law; and upon these leaders rests a fearful responsibility for the iniquity that exists in the Christian world.

(15) WHAT DOES SCRIPTURE PREDICT THE BEAST POWER WOULD ATTEMPT TO CHANGE?

____

____

____

Daniel 7:25

(16) OF WHAT SUBTLE FALSEHOODS WHICH TAKE THE PLACE OF TRUTH ARE WE WARNED?

____

____

____

Colossians 2:8

Yet this very class has put forth the claim that the fast-spreading corruption is largely attributable to the desecration of the so-called "Christian sabbath," and that the enforcement of Sunday observance would greatly improve the morals of society. This claim is especially urged in America, where the doctrine of the true Sabbath [seventh day of the week = Exodus 20:8-11] has been most widely preached. Here the temperance work, one of the most prominent and important of moral reforms, is often combined with the Sunday movement, and the advocates of the latter represent themselves as laboring to promote the highest interest of society; and those who refuse to unite with them are denounced as the enemies of temperance and reform. But the fact that a movement to establish error is connected with a work which is in itself good, is not an argument in favor of the error. We may disguise poison by mingling it with wholesome food, but we do not change its nature. On the contrary, it is rendered more dangerous, as it is more likely to be taken unawares. It is one of Satan's devices to combine with falsehood just enough truth to give it plausibility. The leaders of the Sunday movement may advocate reforms which the people need, principles which are in harmony with the Bible; yet while there is with these a requirement which is contrary to God's law, His servants cannot unite with them. Nothing can justify them in setting aside the commandments of God for the precepts of men.

(17) WHAT IS THE ULTIMATE RESULT OF PARTIAL OBEDIENCE?

____

____

____

2 Timothy 3:5; Revelation 3:14-16

The line of distinction between professed Christians and the ungodly is now hardly distinguishable. Church members love what the world loves and are ready to join with them, and Satan determines to unite them in one body and thus strengthen his cause by sweeping all into the ranks of spiritualism. Papists, who boast of miracles as a certain sign of the true church, will be readily deceived by this wonderworking power; and Protestants, having cast away the shield of truth, will also be deluded. Papists, Protestants, and worldlings will alike accept the form of godliness without the power, and they will see in this union a grand movement for the conversion of the world and the ushering in of the long-expected millennium.

(18) WHAT WILL BE THE ULTIMATE RESULT OF MANKIND'S REJECTION OF GOD'S LAW?

____

____

____

____

Isaiah 24:4,5

Satan works through the elements also to garner his harvest of unprepared souls. He has studied the secrets of the laboratories of nature, and he uses all his power to control the elements as far as God allows. When he was suffered to afflict Job, how quickly flocks and herds, servants, houses, children, were swept away, one trouble succeeding another as in a moment. It is God that shields His creatures and hedges them in from the power of the destroyer. But the Christian world have shown contempt for the law of Jehovah; and the Lord will do just what He has declared that He would—He will withdraw His blessings from the earth and remove His protecting care from those who are rebelling against His law and teaching and forcing others to do the same. Satan has control of all whom God does not especially guard. He will favor and prosper some in order to further his own designs, and he will bring trouble upon others and lead men to believe that it is God who is afflicting them.

While appearing to the children of men as a great physician who can heal all their maladies, he will bring disease and disaster, until populous cities are reduced to ruin and desolation. Even now he is at work. In accidents and calamities by sea and by land, in great conflagrations, in fierce tornadoes and terrific hailstorms, in tempests, floods, cyclones, tidal waves, and earthquakes, in every place and in a thousand forms, Satan is exercising his power. He sweeps away the ripening harvest, and famine and distress follow. He imparts to the air a deadly taint, and thousands perish by the pestilence. These visitations are to become more and more frequent and disastrous. Destruction will be upon both man and beast. "The earth mourneth and fadeth away," "the haughty people . . . do languish. The earth also is defiled under the inhabitants thereof; because they have transgressed the laws, changed the ordinance, broken the everlasting covenant."

(19) WHAT IS THE TERRIBLE RESULT WHEN THE DECEIVED ONES ACT IN ACCORDANCE WITH SATAN'S PLANS?

____

____

____

____

John 16:2

And then the great deceiver will persuade men that those who serve God are causing these evils. The class that have provoked the displeasure of Heaven will charge all their troubles upon those whose obedience to God's commandments is a perpetual reproof to transgressors. It will be declared that men are offending God by the violation of the Sunday sabbath; that this sin has brought calamities which will not cease until Sunday observance shall be strictly enforced; and that those who present the claims of the fourth commandment, thus destroying reverence for Sunday, are troublers of the people, preventing their restoration to divine favor and temporal prosperity. Thus the accusation urged of old against the servant of God will be repeated and upon grounds equally well established: "And it came to pass, when Ahab saw Elijah, that Ahab said unto him, Art thou he that troubleth Israel? And he answered, I have not troubled Israel; but thou, and thy father's house, in that ye have forsaken the commandments of the Lord, and thou hast followed Baalim." 1 Kings 18:17, 18. As the wrath of the people shall be excited by false charges, they will pursue a course toward God's ambassadors very similar to that which apostate Israel pursued toward Elijah.

(20) WHAT POWERFUL SOURCE OF DECEPTION WILL SATAN USE IN THE LAST DAYS TO DECEIVE THE MAJORITY TO HIS CAUSE?

____

____

____

____

Revelation 16:14; Matthew 24:24

The miracle-working power manifested through spiritualism will exert its influence against those who choose to obey God rather than men. Communications from the spirits will declare that God has sent them to convince the rejecters of Sunday of their error, affirming that the laws of the land should be obeyed as the law of God. They will lament the great wickedness in the world and second the testimony of religious teachers that the degraded state of morals is caused by the desecration of Sunday. Great will be the indignation excited against all who refuse to accept their testimony.

Satan's policy in this final conflict with God's people is the same that he employed in the opening of the great controversy in heaven. He professed to be seeking to promote the stability of the divine government, while secretly bending every effort to secure its overthrow. . .

(21) UTILIZING HIS METHODS OF SEDUCTION AND CONTROL, WHAT IS SATAN'S UNDERLYING GOAL IN THIS IMPENDING CONFLICT?

____

____

____

____

1 Peter 5:8

God never forces the will or the conscience; but Satan's constant resort—to gain control of those whom he cannot otherwise seduce—is compulsion by cruelty. Through fear or force he endeavors to rule the conscience and to secure homage to himself. To accomplish this, he works through both religious and secular authorities, moving them to the enforcement of human laws in defiance of the law of God.

(22) WHAT CHARACTERISTIC OF GOD'S LAST DAY REMNANT PEOPLE WILL EXCITE THE HATRED OF SATAN AND HIS FOLLOWERS?

____

____

____

____

Revelation 12:17

Those who honor the Bible Sabbath will be denounced as enemies of law and order, as breaking down the moral restraints of society, causing anarchy and corruption, and calling down the judgments of God upon the earth. Their conscientious scruples will be pronounced obstinacy, stubbornness, and contempt of authority. They will be accused of disaffection toward the government. Ministers who deny the obligation of the divine law will present from the pulpit the duty of yielding obedience to the civil authorities as ordained of God. In legislative halls and courts of justice, commandment keepers will be misrepresented and condemned. A false coloring will be given to their words; the worst construction will be put upon their motives.

(23) WHAT ACTION WILL BE TAKEN BY THE CIVIL AUTHORITIES AND ENDORSED BY THE RELIGIOUS MAJORITY IN AN ATTEMPT TO FORCE GOD'S COMMANDMENT KEEPERS TO VIOLATE THEIR CONSCIENCE?

____

____

____

____

Revelation 13:17

As the Protestant churches reject the clear, Scriptural arguments in defense of

God's law, they will long to silence those whose faith they cannot overthrow by the Bible. Though they blind their own eyes to the fact, they are now adopting a course which will lead to the persecution of those who conscientiously refuse to do what the rest of the Christian world are doing, and acknowledge the claims of the papal sabbath.

The dignitaries of church and state will unite to bribe, persuade, or compel all classes to honor the Sunday. The lack of divine authority will be supplied by oppressive enactments. Political corruption is destroying love of justice and regard for truth; and even in free America, rulers and legislators, in order to secure public favor, will yield to the popular demand for a law enforcing Sunday observance. Liberty of conscience, which has cost so great a sacrifice, will no longer be respected. In the soon-coming conflict we shall see exemplified the prophet's words: "The dragon was wroth with the woman, and went to make war with the remnant of her seed, which keep the commandments of God, and have the testimony of Jesus Christ." Revelation 12:17.

[See Appendix B, C, D for a detailed explanation of the history of the Bible Sabbath and man's attempt to change it.]

I am now aware that Scripture describes clearly an impending conflict "such as never was" which will begin as we approach the close of this world's history.

Circle: Yes Undecided

I realize that since the conception of sin the focus of Satan's attack in this great controversy has been God's eternally sacred laws–the basis of His government.

Circle: Yes Undecided

Revelation 12:17 reveals that Satan's ultimate goal is the defamation of God's laws for the purpose of causing the ultimate rejection of these sacred principles.

Circle: Yes Undecided

I now know that Scripture reveals that God's commandments are sacred and eternal despite Satan's and man's attempt to "think to change times and laws." Daniel 7:25.

Circle: Yes Undecided

I now see that the Bible teaches the importance of observance of all of God's sacred commandments and to break one is to break them all. James 2:10.

Circle: Yes Undecided

I choose to be among the loyal remnant people of God who obey His commandments and remain faithful to Jesus. Revelation 14:12.

Circle: Yes Undecided

The Scriptures a Safeguard - 8

(1) WHAT WILL BE OUR SAFEGUARD FROM SATAN'S DELUSIONS?

____

____

____

Luke 4:4; Isaiah 8:20

The people of God are directed to the Scriptures as their safeguard against the influence of false teachers and the delusive power of spirits of darkness. Satan employs every possible device to prevent men from obtaining a knowledge of the Bible; for its plain utterances reveal his deceptions. At every revival of God's work the prince of evil is aroused to more intense activity; he is now putting forth his utmost efforts for a final struggle against Christ and His followers. The last great delusion is soon to open before us. Antichrist is to perform his marvelous works in our sight. So closely will the counterfeit resemble the true that it will be impossible to distinguish between them except by the Holy Scriptures. By their testimony every statement and every miracle must be tested.

(2) FROM WHAT SOURCE WILL OUR STRENGTH COME TO OBEY GOD OVER MAN?

____

____

1 Peter 5:10

Those who endeavor to obey all the commandments of God will be opposed and derided. They can stand only in God. In order to endure the trial before them, they must understand the will of God as revealed in His word; they can honor Him only as they have a right conception of His character, government, and purposes, and act in accordance with them. None but those who have fortified the mind with the truths of the Bible will stand through the last great conflict. To every soul will come the searching test: Shall I obey God rather than men? The decisive hour is even now at hand. Are our feet planted on the rock of God's immutable word? Are we prepared to stand firm in defense of the commandments of God and the faith of Jesus?

(3) WHY HAS GOD PROVIDED PROPHECY IN HIS WORD?

____

____

____

____

____

Romans 15:4; Deuteronomy 29:29; 2 Timothy 3:15

Before His crucifixion the Saviour explained to His disciples that He was to be put to death and to rise again from the tomb, and angels were present to impress His words on minds and hearts. But the disciples were looking for temporal deliverance from the Roman yoke, and they could not tolerate the thought that He in whom all their hopes centered should suffer an ignominious death. The words which they needed to remember were banished from their minds; and when the time of trial came, it found them unprepared. The death of Jesus as fully destroyed their hopes as if He had not forewarned them. So in the prophecies the future is opened before us as plainly as it was opened to the disciples by the words of Christ. The events connected with the close of probation and the work of preparation for the time of trouble, are clearly presented. But multitudes have no more understanding of these important truths than if they had never been revealed. Satan watches to catch away every impression that would make them wise unto salvation, and the time of trouble will find them unready.

(4) WHAT THREE FINAL DAY WARNINGS ARE OUR WAKE-UP CALL TO THE WAY OF SALVATION?

____

____

____

____

____

Revelation 14:6,7

____

____

____

____

____

Revelation 14:8

____

____

____

____

____

Revelation 14:9,10

When God sends to men warnings so important that they are represented as proclaimed by holy angels flying in the midst of heaven, He requires every person endowed with reasoning powers to heed the message. The fearful judgments denounced against the worship of the beast and his image (Revelation 14:9-11), should lead all to a diligent study of the prophecies to learn what the mark of the beast is, and how they are to avoid receiving it. But the masses of the people turn away their ears from hearing the truth and are turned unto fables.

(5) HOW DID PAUL DESCRIBE THE ATTITUDE OF THE LUST DRIVEN MAJORITY TOWARD DOCTRINAL TRUTH?

____

____

____

____

____

2 Timothy 4:3,4

That time has fully come. The multitudes do not want Bible truth, because it interferes with the desires of the sinful, world-loving heart; and Satan supplies the deceptions which they love.

(6) HOW DO CHRIST'S TRUE FOLLOWERS DETERMINE DOCTRINAL TRUTH?

____

____

____

____

Isaiah 8:20

But God will have a people upon the earth to maintain the Bible, and the Bible only, as the standard of all doctrines and the basis of all reforms. The opinions of learned men, the deductions of science, the creeds or decisions of ecclesiastical councils, as numerous and discordant as are the churches which they represent, the voice of the majority—not one nor all of these should be regarded as evidence for or against any point of religious faith. Before accepting any doctrine or precept, we should demand a plain "Thus saith the Lord" in its support.

(7) WHAT HAS OUR RESPONSIBILITY TO DO WITH THE TEACHINGS OF MEN?

____

____

____

Acts 17:11

Satan is constantly endeavoring to attract attention to man in the place of God. He leads the people to look to bishops, to pastors, to professors of theology, as their guides, instead of searching the Scriptures to learn their duty for themselves. Then, by controlling the minds of these leaders, he can influence the multitudes according to his will.

(8) WHAT WAS THE RESULT OF THE JEWISH NATION'S RELIANCE ON THEIR LEADERS FOR UNDERSTANDING SCRIPTURE?

____

____

____

Isaiah 53:3

When Christ came to speak the words of life, the common people heard Him gladly; and many, even of the priests and rulers, believed on Him. But the chief of the priesthood and the leading men of the nation were determined to condemn and repudiate His teachings. Though they were baffled in all their efforts to find accusations against Him, though they could not but feel the influence of the divine power and wisdom attending His words, yet they encased themselves in prejudice; they rejected the clearest evidence of His Messiahship, lest they should be forced to become His disciples. These opponents of Jesus were men whom the people had been taught from infancy to reverence, to whose authority they had been accustomed implicitly to bow. "How is it," they asked, "that our rulers and learned scribes do not believe on Jesus? Would not these pious men receive Him if He were the Christ?" It was the influence of such teachers that led the Jewish nation to reject their Redeemer.

The spirit which actuated those priests and rulers is still manifested by many who make a high profession of piety. They refuse to examine the testimony of the Scriptures concerning the special truths for this time. They point to their own numbers, wealth, and popularity, and look with contempt upon the advocates of truth as few, poor, and unpopular, having a faith that separates them from the world.

(9) WHAT IS THE ONLY SOURCE OF PREVENTION AGAINST DECEPTION?

____

____

____

____

____

____

2 Timothy 2:15

Christ foresaw that the undue assumption of authority indulged by the scribes and Pharisees would not cease with the dispersion of the Jews. He had a prophetic view of the work of exalting human authority to rule the conscience, which has been so terrible a curse to the church in all ages. And His fearful denunciations of the scribes and Pharisees, and His warnings to the people not to follow these blind leaders, were placed on record as an admonition to future generations.

(10) ACCORDING TO SCRIPTURE WHO WILL BE AMONG US SOWING FALSE DOCTRINE?

____

____

____

2 Peter 2:1

Notwithstanding the Bible is full of warnings against false teachers, many are ready thus to commit the keeping of their souls to the clergy. There are today thousands of professors of religion who can give no other reason for points of faith which they hold than that they were so instructed by their religious leaders. They pass by the Saviour's teachings almost unnoticed, and place implicit confidence in the words of the ministers. But are ministers infallible? How can we trust our souls to their guidance unless we know from God's word that they are light bearers? A lack of moral courage to step aside from the beaten track of the world leads many to follow in the steps of learned men; and by their reluctance to investigate for themselves, they are becoming hopelessly fastened in the chains of error. They see that the truth for this time is plainly brought to view in the Bible; and they feel the power of the Holy Spirit attending its proclamation; yet they allow the opposition of the clergy to turn them from the light. Though reason and conscience are convinced, these deluded souls dare not think differently from the minister; and their individual judgment, their eternal interests, are sacrificed to the unbelief, the pride and prejudice, of another.

(11) UPON WHOM DOES THE RESPONSIBILITY FOR SEEKING THE TRUTHS OF SALVATION REST?

____

____

____

____

Philippians 2:12

The truth and the glory of God are inseparable; it is impossible for us, with the Bible within our reach, to honor God by erroneous opinions. Many claim that it matters not what one believes, if his life is only right. But the life is molded by the faith. If light and truth is within our reach, and we neglect to improve the privilege of hearing and seeing it, we virtually reject it; we are choosing darkness rather than light.

(12) WHY IS IGNORANCE OF THE SCRIPTURES DANGEROUS?

____

____

____

____

____

Proverbs 16:25

Ignorance is no excuse for error or sin, when there is every opportunity to know the will of God. A man is traveling and comes to a place where there are several roads and a guideboard indicating where each one leads. If he disregards the guideboard, and takes whichever road seems to him to be right, he may be ever so sincere, but will in all probability find himself on the wrong road.

God has given us His word that we may become acquainted with its teachings and know for ourselves what He requires of us. When the lawyer came to Jesus with the inquiry, "What shall I do to inherit eternal life?" the Saviour referred him to the Scriptures, saying: "What is written in the law? how readest thou?" Ignorance will not excuse young or old, nor release them from the punishment due for the transgression of God's law; because there is in their hands a faithful presentation of that law and of its principles and claims. It is not enough to have good intentions; it is not enough to do what a man thinks is right or what the minister tells him is right. His soul's salvation is at stake, and he should search the Scriptures for himself. However strong may be his convictions, however confident he may be that the minister knows what is truth, this is not his foundation. He has a chart pointing out every waymark on the heavenward journey, and he ought not to guess at anything.

(13) HOW DOES SCRIPTURE POINT OUT THE WAY TO STUDY ITS PAGES?

____

____

____

____

Isaiah 28:10

It is the first and highest duty of every rational being to learn from the Scriptures what is truth, and then to walk in the light and encourage others to follow his example. We should day by day study the Bible diligently, weighing every thought and comparing scripture with scripture. With divine help we are to form our opinions for ourselves as we are to answer for ourselves before God.

(14) IF WE SEARCH THE BIBLE SEEKING TO DO GOD'S WILL WHAT PROMISE MAY WE CLAIM?

____

____

____

John 7:17

The truths most plainly revealed in the Bible have been involved in doubt and darkness by learned men, who, with a pretense of great wisdom, teach that the Scriptures have a mystical, a secret, spiritual meaning not apparent in the language employed. These men are false teachers. It was to such a class that Jesus declared: "Ye know not the Scriptures, neither the power of God." Mark 12:24. The language of the Bible should be explained according to its obvious meaning, unless a symbol or figure is employed. Christ has given the promise: "If any man will do His will, he shall know of the doctrine." John 7:17. If men would but take the Bible as it reads, if there were no false teachers to mislead and confuse their minds, a work would be accomplished that would make angels glad and that would bring into the fold of Christ thousands upon thousands who are now wandering in error.

(15) WHAT STEPS WILL YIELD CHRIST'S PROMISED RESULTS?

____

____

Jeremiah 29:12

____

____

Jeremiah 29:13

We should exert all the powers of the mind in the study of the Scriptures and should task the understanding to comprehend, as far as mortals can, the deep things of God; yet we must not forget that the docility and submission of a child is the true spirit of the learner. Scriptural difficulties can never be mastered by the same methods that are employed in grappling with philosophical problems. We should not engage in the study of the Bible with that self-reliance with which so many enter the domains of science, but with a prayerful dependence upon God and a sincere desire to learn His will. We must come with a humble and teachable spirit to obtain knowledge from the great I AM. Otherwise, evil angels will so blind our minds and harden our hearts that we shall not be impressed by the truth.

(16) TO WHOM IS BIBLICAL WISDOM PROMISED?

____

____

____

John 8:31,32; Psalm 19:7

Many a portion of Scripture which learned men pronounce a mystery, or pass over as unimportant, is full of comfort and instruction to him who has been taught in the school of Christ. One reason why many theologians have no clearer understanding of God's word is, they close their eyes to truths which they do not wish to practice. As understanding of Bible truth depends not so much on the power of intellect brought to the search as on the singleness of purpose, the earnest longing after righteousness.

(17) HOW ARE SPIRITUAL TRUTHS UNDERSTOOD?

____

____

1 Corinthians 2:14

The Bible should never be studied without prayer. The Holy Spirit alone can cause us to feel the importance of those things easy to be understood, or prevent us from wresting truths difficult of comprehension. It is the office of heavenly angels to prepare the heart so to comprehend God's word that we shall be charmed with its beauty, admonished by its warnings, or animated and strengthened by its promises. We should make the psalmist's petition our own: "Open Thou mine eyes, that I may behold wondrous things out of Thy law." Psalm 119:18. Temptations often appear irresistible because, through neglect of prayer and the study of the Bible, the tempted one cannot readily remember God's promises and meet Satan with the Scripture weapons. But angels are round about those who are willing to be taught in divine things; and in the time of great necessity they will bring to their remembrance the very truths which are needed. Thus "when the enemy shall come in like a flood, the Spirit of the Lord shall lift up a standard against him." Isaiah 59:19.

(18) IN PERILOUS TIMES HOW WILL WE RECALL SPIRITUAL TRUTHS?

____

____

____

____

____

John 14:26

But the teachings of Christ must previously have been stored in the mind in order for the Spirit of God to bring them to our remembrance in the time of peril. "Thy word have I hid in mine heart," said David, "that I might not sin against Thee." Psalm 119:11.

(19) WHAT IS THE TRAGIC RESULT OF SKEPTICISM OF GOD'S WORD?

____

____

____

Romans 1:28; Hebrews 3:12

All who value their eternal interests should be on their guard against the inroads of skepticism. The very pillars of truth will be assailed. It is impossible to keep beyond the reach of the sarcasms and sophisms, the insidious and pestilent teachings, of modern infidelity. Satan adapts his temptations to all classes. He assails the illiterate with a jest or sneer, while he meets the educated with scientific objections and philosophical reasoning, alike calculated to excite distrust or contempt of the Scriptures. Even youth of little experience presume to insinuate doubts concerning the fundamental principles of Christianity. And this youthful infidelity, shallow as it is, has its influence. Many are thus led to jest at the faith of their fathers and to do despite to the Spirit of grace. Hebrews 10:29. Many a life that promised to be an honor to God and a blessing to the world has been blighted by the foul breath of infidelity. All who trust to the boastful decisions of human reason and imagine that they can explain divine mysteries and arrive at truth unaided by the wisdom of God are entangled in the snare of Satan.

(20) IF WE HAVE MADE GOD'S WORD OUR STRONGHOLD WHAT WILL BE THE RESULT OF OUR TRIALS?

____

____

____

____

____

____

____

____

Zechariah 13:9; Psalm 119:99,104; Proverbs 3:13; Jeremiah 17:8.

When the testing time shall come, those who have made God's word their rule of life will be revealed. In summer there is no noticeable difference between evergreens and other trees; but when the blasts of winter come, the evergreens remain unchanged, while other trees are stripped of their foliage. So the falsehearted professor may not now be distinguished from the real Christian, but the time is just upon us when the difference will be apparent. Let opposition arise, let bigotry and intolerance again bear sway, let persecution be kindled, and the halfhearted and hypocritical will waver and yield the faith; but the true Christian will stand firm as a rock, his faith stronger, his hope brighter, than in days of prosperity.

I realize that in the final days of earth's history Satan is employing every possible device to prevent mankind from obtaining knowledge of God's holy Word.

Circle: Yes Undecided

I understand that those who endeavor to obey all the commandments of God will be opposed and derided and can only stand by strength gleaned from God's Word.

Circle: Yes Undecided

I realize that the day is here where the lust driven majority do not want Bible truth because it interferes with the desires of their sinful, world-loving hearts. They gladly are accepting the deceptions of Satan which they love.

Circle: Yes Undecided

I see in God's Word that in the last days there will be many false teachers proclaiming false doctrines. I am thankful to the Lord for providing the prophecies to make us wise unto salvation.

Circle: Yes Undecided

It is my determination that with God's help I will have my own daily study of God's Word and not depend on others for its interpretation.

Circle: Yes Undecided

I thank God for providing the stronghold of His Word in these times of testing and by His grace I will be among those who are obedient to His Word and stand tall in the day of His coming.

Circle: Yes Undecided

The Final Warning - 9

(1) WHAT FINAL DAY MESSAGE OF WARNING IS PROCLAIMED BY THE "ANGEL" OF REVELATION 14:8?

____

____

____

____

Revelation 14:8; Revelation 18:1,2

(2) WHEN THIS WARNING IS RESTATED BY JOHN IN REVELATION 18 WHAT PLEA IS GIVEN TO GOD'S LOYAL FOLLOWERS?

____

____

____

____

____

Revelation 18:4

This scripture points forward to a time when the announcement of the fall of Babylon, as made by the second angel of Revelation 14:8 is to be repeated, with the additional mention of the corruptions which have been entering the various organizations that constitute Babylon, since that message was first given, in the summer of 1844. A terrible condition of the religious world is here described. With every rejection of truth the minds of the people will become darker, their hearts more stubborn, until they are entrenched in an infidel hardihood. In defiance of the warnings which God has given, they will continue to trample upon one of the precepts of the Decalogue, until they are led to persecute those who hold it sacred. Christ is set at nought in the contempt placed upon His word and His people. As the teachings of spiritualism are accepted by the churches, the restraint imposed upon the carnal heart is removed, and the profession of religion will become a cloak to conceal the basest iniquity. A belief in spiritual manifestations opens the door to seducing spirits and doctrines of devils, and thus the influence of evil angels will be felt in the churches.

(3) TO WHAT LEVEL DO THE "SINS" OF BABYLON ESCALATE?

____

____

____

Revelation 18:5

She has filled up the measure of her guilt, and destruction is about to fall upon her. But God still has a people in Babylon; and before the visitation of His judgments these faithful ones must be called out, that they partake not of her sins and "receive not of her plagues." Hence the movement symbolized by the angel coming down from heaven, lightening the earth with his glory and crying mightily with a strong voice, announcing the sins of Babylon. In connection with his message the call is heard: "Come out of her, My people." These announcements, uniting with the third angel's message, constitute the final warning to be given to the inhabitants of the earth.

(4) WHAT PENALTIES WILL THE BEAST POWER IMAGE INFLICT UPON GOD'S REMNANT WHO REFUSE TO PARTICIPATE IN HER FALSE DOCTRINES?

____

____

____

Revelation 13:17

____

____

____

Revelation 13:15

Fearful is the issue to which the world is to be brought. The powers of earth, uniting to war against the commandments of God, will decree that "all, both small and great, rich and poor, free and bond" (Revelation 13:16), shall conform to the customs of the church by the observance of the false sabbath [See Appendix B, C, D]. All who refuse compliance will be visited with civil penalties, and it will finally be declared that they are deserving of death [See Appendix F].

(5) WHAT WARNING MESSAGE DOES GOD PROCLAIM THROUGH THE THIRD ANGEL TO THOSE WHO CHOOSE TO WORSHIP THE BEAST?

____

____

____

____

Revelation 14:9,10

On the other hand, the law of God enjoining the Creator's rest day [Exodus 20:8-11; Hebrew 4:1-11] demands obedience and threatens wrath against all who transgress its precepts.

With the issue thus clearly brought before him, whoever shall trample upon God's law to obey a human enactment receives the mark of the beast; he accepts the sign of allegiance to the power which he chooses to obey instead of God.

But not one is made to suffer the wrath of God until the truth has been brought home to his mind and conscience, and has been rejected. There are many who have never had an opportunity to hear the special truths for this time. The obligation of the fourth commandment has never been set before them in its true light. He who reads every heart and tries every motive will leave none who desire a knowledge of the truth, to be deceived as to the issues of the controversy. The decree is not to be urged upon the people blindly. Everyone is to have sufficient light to make his decision intelligently.

(6) ACCORDING TO SCRIPTURE WHAT DOES THE SABBATH OF THE FOURTH COMMANDMENT REPRESENT?

____

____

____

____

Ezekiel 20:20,12; Exodus 31:16,17

The Sabbath will be the great test of loyalty, for it is the point of truth especially controverted. When the final test shall be brought to bear upon men, then the line of distinction will be drawn between those who serve God and those who serve Him not. While the observance of the false sabbath in compliance with the law of the state, contrary to the fourth commandment, will be an avowal of allegiance to a power that is in opposition to God, the keeping of the true Sabbath, in obedience to God's law, is an evidence of loyalty to the Creator. While one class, by accepting the sign of submission to earthly powers, receive the mark of the beast, the other choosing the token of allegiance to divine authority, receive the seal of God.

Heretofore those who presented the truths of the third angel's message have often been regarded as mere alarmists. Their predictions that religious intolerance would gain control in the United States, that church and state would unite to persecute those who keep the commandments of God, have been pronounced groundless and absurd. It has been confidently declared that this land could never become other than what it has been—the defender of religious freedom. But as the question of enforcing Sunday observance is widely agitated, the event so long doubted and disbelieved is seen to be approaching, and the third message will produce an effect which it could not have had before.

(7) WHO DOES GOD CONSIDER TO BE THE "CHILDREN OF ISRAEL?"

____

____

____

____

Romans 9:6-8; Romans 9:25-27

(8) IN THE LAST DAYS WHO WILL THE LUST SEEKING MAJOR -ITY TURN TO FOR SPIRITUAL LEADERSHIP?

____

____

____

2 Timothy 4:3,4

(9) HOW SHOULD GOD'S ENDTIME MESSAGE BE DELIVERED?

____

____

____

2 Timothy 4:2

In every generation God has sent His servants to rebuke sin, both in the world and in the church. But the people desire smooth things spoken to them, and the pure, unvarnished truth is not acceptable. Many reformers, in entering upon their work, determined to exercise great prudence in attacking the sins of the church and the nation. They hoped, by the example of a pure Christian life, to lead the people back to the doctrines of the Bible. But the Spirit of God came upon them as it came upon Elijah, moving him to rebuke the sins of a wicked king and an apostate people; they could not refrain from preaching the plain utterances of the Bible—doctrines which they had been reluctant to present. They were impelled to zealously declare the truth and the danger which threatened souls. The words which the Lord gave them they uttered, fearless of consequences, and the people were compelled to hear the warning.

(10) WHO WILL GOD USE TO DELIVER THE THREE ANGELS MESSAGES OF REVELATION 14 TO THE WORLD?

____

____

____

John 15:14-16; Matthew 28:19,20; Ezekiel 3:19; Acts 4:20

Thus the message of the third angel will be proclaimed. As the time comes for it to be given with greatest power, the Lord will work through humble instruments, leading the minds of those who consecrate themselves to His service. The laborers will be qualified rather by the unction of His Spirit than by the training of literary institutions. Men of faith and prayer will be constrained to go forth with holy zeal, declaring the words which God gives them.

(11) WHEN THE FALSE DOCTRINES OF BABYLON ARE REVEALED, WHAT PROMISE CAN THOSE WHO EARNESTLY SEEK TO FOLLOW THE TRUE DOCTRINES OF CHRIST CLAIM?

____

____

____

____

John 8:31,32

The sins of Babylon will be laid open. The fearful results of enforcing the observances of the church by civil authority, the inroads of spiritualism, the stealthy but rapid progress of the papal power—all will be unmasked. By these solemn warnings the people will be stirred. Thousands upon thousands will listen who have never heard words like these. In amazement they hear the testimony that Babylon is the church, fallen because of her errors and sins, because of her rejection of the truth sent to her from heaven. As the people go to their former teachers with the eager inquiry, Are these things so? the ministers present fables, prophesy smooth things, to soothe their fears and quiet the awakened conscience. But since many refuse to be satisfied with the mere authority of men and demand a plain "Thus saith the Lord," the popular ministry, like the Pharisees of old, filled with anger as their authority is questioned, will denounce the message as of Satan and stir up the sin-loving multitudes to revile and persecute those who proclaim it.

(12) WHAT PROPHECY IN THIS VERSE WILL BE FULFILLED AGAINST THOSE WHO CHOOSE OBEDIENCE TO GOD'S COMMANDMENTS OVER THE FALSE DOCTRINES OF BABYLON?

____

____

____

____

Revelation 12:17; Mark 13:9-11

As the controversy extends into new fields and the minds of the people are called to God's downtrodden law, Satan is astir. The power attending the message will only madden those who oppose it. The clergy will put forth almost superhuman efforts to shut away the light lest it should shine upon their flocks. By every means at their command they will endeavor to suppress the discussion of these vital questions. The church appeals to the strong arm of civil power, and, in this work, papists and Protestants unite. As the movement for Sunday enforcement becomes more bold and decided, the law will be invoked against commandment keepers. They will be threatened with fines and imprisonment, and some will be offered positions of influence, and other rewards and advantages, as inducements to renounce their faith. But their steadfast answer is: "Show us from the word of God our error"—the same plea that was made by Luther under similar circumstances. Those who are arraigned before the courts make a strong vindication of the truth, and some who hear them are led to take their stand to keep all the commandments of God. Thus light will be brought before thousands who otherwise would know nothing of these truths. Conscientious obedience to the word of God will be treated as rebellion.

(13) WHAT WILL HAPPEN EVEN BETWEEN FAMILY MEMBERS BECAUSE SOME CHOOSE OBEDIENCE TO THE TRUTH?

____

____

____

Mark 13:12

Blinded by Satan, the parent will exercise harshness and severity toward the believing child; the master or mistress will oppress the commandment-keeping servant. Affection will be alienated; children will be disinherited and driven from home. The words of Paul will be literally fulfilled: "All that will live godly in Christ Jesus shall suffer persecution." 2 Timothy 3:12. As the defenders of truth refuse to honor the Sunday-sabbath, some of them will be thrust into prison, some will be exiled, some will be treated as slaves. To human wisdom all this now seems impossible; but as the restraining Spirit of God shall be withdrawn from men, and they shall be under the control of Satan, who hates the divine precepts, there will be strange developments. The heart can be very cruel when God's fear and love are removed.

(14) WHAT MUST ACCOMPANY OUR KNOWLEDGE OF TRUTH TO KEEP US FROM BECOMING ITS GREATEST ADVERSARY?

____

____

____

1 John 2:4,5; John 8:31,32

As the storm approaches, a large class who have professed faith in the third angel's message, but have not been sanctified through obedience to the truth, abandon their position and join the ranks of the opposition. By uniting with the world and partaking of its spirit, they have come to view matters in nearly the same light; and when the test is brought, they are prepared to choose the easy, popular side. Men of talent and pleasing address, who once rejoiced in the truth, employ their powers to deceive and mislead souls. They become the most bitter enemies of their former brethren. When Sabbathkeepers are brought before the courts to answer for their faith, these apostates are the most efficient agents of Satan to misrepresent and accuse them, and by false reports and insinuations to stir up the rulers against them.

(15) LIKE PETER AND JOHN, WHAT WILL BE THE DECISION OF THOSE SUFFERING PERSECUTION WHEN PROCLAIMING TRUTH?

____

____

____

Acts 4:19

In this time of persecution the faith of the Lord's servants will be tried. They have faithfully given the warning, looking to God and to His word alone. God's Spirit, moving upon their hearts, has constrained them to speak. Stimulated with holy zeal, and with the divine impulse strong upon them, they entered upon the performance of their duties without coldly calculating the consequences of speaking to the people the word which the Lord had given them. They have not consulted their temporal interests, nor sought to preserve their reputation or their lives. Yet when the storm of opposition and reproach bursts upon them, some, overwhelmed with consternation, will be ready to exclaim: "Had we foreseen the consequences of our words, we would have held our peace." They are hedged in with difficulties. Satan assails them with fierce temptations. The work which they have undertaken seems far beyond their ability to accomplish. They are threatened with destruction. The enthusiasm which animated them is gone; yet they cannot turn back. Then, feeling their utter helplessness, they flee to the Mighty One for strength. They remember that the words which they have spoken were not theirs, but His who bade them give the warning. God put the truth into their hearts, and they could not forbear to proclaim it.

(16) IN THESE MOMENTS OF PERIL FROM WHOM CAN WE DRAW STRENGTH?

____

____

____

____

____

Isaiah 40:28-31; Psalm 46

As the opposition rises to a fiercer height, the servants of God are again perplexed; for it seems to them that they have brought the crisis. But conscience and the word of God assure them that their course is right; and although the trials continue, they are strengthened to bear them. The contest grows closer and sharper, but their faith and courage rise with the emergency. Their testimony is: "We dare not tamper with God's word, dividing His holy law; calling one portion essential and another nonessential, to gain the favor of the world. The Lord whom we serve is able to deliver us.

Christ has conquered the powers of earth; and shall we be afraid of a world already conquered?"

(17) WHEN WE SERVE CHRIST WITHOUT RESERVATION, WHAT TREATMENT CAN BE EXPECTED?

____

____

____

Matthew 24:9; Psalm 11:2

Persecution in its varied forms is the development of a principle which will exist as long as Satan exists and Christianity has vital power. No man can serve God without enlisting against himself the opposition of the hosts of darkness. Evil angels will assail him, alarmed that his influence is taking the prey from their hands. Evil men, rebuked by his example, will unite with them in seeking to separate him from God by alluring temptations. When these do not succeed, then a compelling power is employed to force the conscience.

(18) EVEN IN THESE PERILOUS TIMES, WHO ULTIMATELY CONTROLS EARTHLY RULERS?

____

____

____

____

Proverbs 21:1; Romans 13:1

But so long as Jesus remains man's intercessor in the sanctuary above, the restraining influence of the Holy Spirit is felt by rulers and people. It still controls to some extent the laws of the land. Were it not for these laws, the condition of the world would be much worse than it now is. While many of our rulers are active agents of Satan, God also has His agents among the leading men of the nation. The enemy moves upon his servants to propose measures that would greatly impede the work of God; but statesmen who fear the Lord are influenced by holy angels to oppose such propositions with unanswerable arguments. Thus a few men will hold in check a powerful current of evil. The opposition of the enemies of truth will be restrained that the third angel's message may do its work. When the final warning shall be given, it will arrest the attention of these leading men through whom the Lord is now working, and some of them will accept it, and will stand with the people of God through the time of trouble.

(19) WHO WILL GOD SEND TO MOVE THE HEARTS OF MEN TO ACCEPT HIS LAST DAY WARNING MESSAGE?

____

____

Acts 2:17; Joel 2:28

The work will be similar to that of the Day of Pentecost. As the "former rain" was given, in the outpouring of the Holy Spirit at the opening of the gospel, to cause the upspringing of the precious seed, so the "latter rain" will be given at its close for the ripening of the harvest. "Then shall we know, if we follow on to know the Lord: His going forth is prepared as the morning; and He shall come unto us as the rain, as the latter and former rain unto the earth." Hosea 6:3. "Be glad then, ye children of Zion, and rejoice in the Lord your God: for He hath given you the former rain moderately, and He will cause to come down for you the rain, the former rain, and the latter rain." Joel 2:23.

The great work of the gospel is not to close with less manifestation of the power of God than marked its opening. The prophecies which were fulfilled in the outpouring of the former rain at the opening of the gospel are again to be fulfilled in the latter rain at its close. Here are "the times of refreshing" to which the apostle Peter looked forward when he said: "Repent ye therefore, and be converted, that your sins may be blotted out, when the times of refreshing shall come from the presence of the Lord; and He shall send Jesus." Acts 3:19, 20.

(20) AS SIGNS AND WONDERS GO OUT FROM GOD TO IMPACT HIS WARNING MESSAGE, WHAT WILL SATAN ALSO DO THROUGH HIS AGENTS IN AN EFFORT TO REFUTE THE POWER OF GOD'S SPIRIT AND DECEIVE THE MULTITUDES?

____

____

____

Revelation 13:13

Servants of God, with their faces lighted up and shining with holy consecration, will hasten from place to place to proclaim the message from heaven. By thousands of voices, all over the earth, the warning will be given. Miracles will be wrought, the sick will be healed, and signs and wonders will follow the believers [Acts 2:19]. Satan also works, with lying wonders, even bringing down fire from heaven in the sight of men. Thus the inhabitants of the earth will be brought to take their stand.

(21) WHAT WILL BE THE RESULT OF GOD'S SPIRIT CONVICTING HEARTS OF THE FINAL WARNING MESSAGE?

____

____

Acts 2:17-21

The message will be carried not so much by argument as by the deep conviction of the Spirit of God. The arguments have been presented. The seed has been sown, and now it will spring up and bear fruit. The publications distributed by missionary workers have exerted their influence, yet many whose minds were impressed have been prevented from fully comprehending the truth or from yielding obedience. Now the rays of light penetrate everywhere, the truth is seen in its clearness, and the honest children of God sever the bands which have held them. Family connections, church relations, are powerless to stay them now. Truth is more precious than all besides. Notwithstanding the agencies combined against the truth, a large number take their stand upon the Lord's side.

I am thankful to the Lord for giving us the warning messages of Revelation 14 to prepare us against deception.

Circle: Yes Undecided

I pray for the Holy Spirit to guide me and remove any preconceived ideas that may hinder my acceptance of the truth.

Circle: Yes Undecided

These warning messages reveal that this great controversy is about loyalty to God. I pray for strength and courage to follow His commandments come what may.

Circle: Yes Undecided

The Time of Trouble - 10

(1) WHAT PROCLAMATION BY CHRIST FROM THE HEAVENLY SANCTUARY WILL MARK THE END OF PROBATION FOR MANKIND?

____

____

____

____

____

Revelation 22:11; Revelation 16:17

When the third angel's message closes [Revelation 14:9,10], mercy no longer pleads for the guilty inhabitants of the earth. The people of God have accomplished their work. They have received "the latter rain," "the refreshing from the presence of the Lord," and they are prepared for the trying hour before them. Angels are hastening to and fro in heaven. An angel returning from the earth announces that his work is done; the final test has been brought upon the world, and all who have proved themselves loyal to the divine precepts [Revelation 14:12] have received "the seal of the living God." Then Jesus ceases His intercession in the sanctuary above. He lifts His hands and with a loud voice says, "It is done;" and all the angelic host lay off their crowns as He makes the solemn announcement: "He that is unjust, let him be unjust still: and he which is filthy, let him be filthy still:

and he that is righteous, let him be righteous still: and he that is holy, let him be holy still." Revelation 22:11. Every case has been decided for life or death. Christ has made the atonement for His people and blotted out their sins. The number of His subjects is made up; "the kingdom and dominion, and the greatness of the kingdom under the whole heaven," is about to be given to the heirs of salvation, and Jesus is to reign as King of kings and Lord of lords [Revelation 17:14].

(2) WHAT CATASTROPHIC EVENT WILL OCCUR BETWEEN THE CLOSE OF PROBATION AND THE FIRST RESURRECTION?

____

____

____

____

Daniel 12:1

When He leaves the sanctuary, darkness covers the inhabitants of the earth. In that fearful time the righteous must live in the sight of a holy God without an intercessor. The restraint which has been upon the wicked is removed, and Satan has entire control of the finally impenitent. God's long-suffering has ended. The world has rejected His mercy, despised His love, and trampled upon His law. The wicked have passed the boundary of their probation; the Spirit of God, persistently resisted, has been at last withdrawn. Unsheltered by divine grace, they have no protection from the wicked one. Satan will then plunge the inhabitants of the earth into one great, final trouble.

(3) WHAT DIVINE AGENCY IS CURRENTLY HOLDING BACK THESE DREADED WINDS OF STRIFE UNTIL THE SEALING OF GOD'S PEOPLE?

____

____

____

Revelation 7:1

As the angels of God cease to hold in check the fierce winds of human passion, all the elements of strife will be let loose. The whole world will be involved in ruin more terrible than that which came upon Jerusalem of old.

A single angel destroyed all the firstborn of the Egyptians and filled the land with mourning. When David offended against God by numbering the people, one angel caused that terrible destruction by which his sin was punished. The same destructive power exercised by holy angels when God commands, will be exercised by evil angels when He permits. There are forces now ready, and only waiting the divine permission, to spread desolation everywhere.

(4) WHAT TWO CHARACTERISTICS OF GOD'S PEOPLE WILL KINDLE UNDUE ANGER AND PERSECUTION IN THE HEARTS OF THE WICKED?

____

____

____

____

Revelation 14:12

Those who honor the law of God have been accused of bringing judgments upon the world, and they will be regarded as the cause of the fearful convulsions of nature and the strife and bloodshed among men that are filling the earth with woe. The power attending the last warning has enraged the wicked; their anger is kindled against all who have received the message, and Satan will excite to still greater intensity the spirit of hatred and persecution.

(5) WHAT SAME SPIRITUAL STATE WILL THE SELF-PROCLAIMED SPIRITUAL MAJORITY POSSESS IN THE LAST DAYS, AS IN CHRIST'S DAY?

____

____

____

____

____

____

Matthew 15:8,9

When God's presence was finally withdrawn from the Jewish nation, priests and people knew it not. Though under the control of Satan, and swayed by the most horrible and malignant passions, they still regarded themselves as the chosen of God. The ministration in the temple continued; sacrifices were offered upon its polluted altars, and daily the divine blessing was invoked upon a people guilty of the blood of God's dear Son and seeking to slay His ministers and apostles. So when the irrevocable decision of the sanctuary has been pronounced and the destiny of the world has been forever fixed, the inhabitants of the earth will know it not. The forms of religion will be continued by a people from whom the Spirit of God has been finally withdrawn; and the satanic zeal with which the prince of evil will inspire them for the accomplishment of his malignant designs, will bear the semblance of zeal for God.

(6) WHAT WILL THE WICKED ATTEMPT TO DO, THINKING IT IS A SERVICE FOR GOD?

____

____

____

John 16:2; Revelation 13:15

As the Sabbath has become the special point of controversy throughout Christendom, and religious and secular authorities have combined to enforce the observance of the Sunday, the persistent refusal of a small minority to yield to the popular demand will make them objects of universal execration. It will be urged that the few who stand in opposition to an institution of the church and a law of the state ought not to be tolerated; that it is better for them to suffer than for whole nations to be thrown into confusion and lawlessness. The same argument eighteen hundred years ago was brought against Christ by the "rulers of the people." "It is expedient for us," said the wily Caiaphas, "that one man should die for the people, and that the whole nation perish not." John 11:50. This argument will appear conclusive; and a decree will finally be issued against those who hallow the Sabbath of the fourth commandment [Exodus 20:8-11], denouncing them as deserving of the severest punishment and giving the people liberty, after a certain time, to put them to death. Romanism in the Old World and apostate Protestantism in the New will pursue a similar course toward those who honor all the divine precepts [See Appendix E, F].

(7) TO WHAT EVENT IS THIS TERRIBLE LAST DAY HOLOCAUST AGAINST GOD'S PEOPLE COMPARED?

____

____

____

Jeremiah 30:7

The people of God will then be plunged into those scenes of affliction and distress described by the prophet as the time of Jacob's trouble. "Thus saith the Lord: We have heard a voice of trembling, of fear, and not of peace. . . . All faces are turned into paleness. Alas! for that day is great, so that none is like it: it is even the time of Jacob's trouble; but he shall be saved out of it." Jeremiah 30:5-7. . . Jacob's night of anguish, when he wrestled in prayer for deliverance from the hand of Esau (Genesis 32:24-30), represents the experience of God's people in the time of trouble. . .

(8) WHO IS THE DRAGON?

____

____

Revelation 12:9

(9) WHAT IS THE DRAGON'S REACTION TOWARDS THOSE WHO ARE LOYAL TO GOD'S COMMANDMENTS?

____

____

____

____

____

Revelation 12:17

As Satan influenced Esau to march against Jacob, so he will stir up the wicked to destroy God's people in the time of trouble. And as he accused Jacob, he will urge his accusations against the people of God. He numbers the world as his subjects; but the little company who keep the commandments of God are resisting his supremacy. If he could blot them from the earth, his triumph would be complete. He sees that holy angels are guarding them, and he infers that their sins have been pardoned; but he does not know that their cases have been decided in the sanctuary above. He has an accurate knowledge of the sins which he has tempted them to commit, and he presents these before God in the most exaggerated light, representing this people to be just as deserving as himself of exclusion from the favor of God. He declares that the Lord cannot in justice forgive their sins and yet destroy him and his angels. He claims them as his prey and demands that they be given into his hands to destroy.

(10) WHAT IMPORTANT ASPECT OF THE CHRISTIAN'S CHARACTER WILL BE TESTED IN THIS PERILOUS TIME?

____

____

1 Peter 1:7; James 1:3

As Satan accuses the people of God on account of their sins, the Lord permits him to try them to the uttermost. Their confidence in God, their faith and firmness, will be severely tested. As they review the past, their hopes sink; for in their whole lives they can see little good. They are fully conscious of their weakness and unworthiness. Satan endeavors to terrify them with the thought that their cases are hopeless, that the stain of their defilement will never be washed away. He hopes so to destroy their faith that they will yield to his temptations and turn from their allegiance to God.

(11) WHAT PROMISE HAS GOD GIVEN TO HIS CHILDREN, WHO THROUGH FAITH, PERSEVERE?

____

____

____

Revelation 3:10; Matthew 10:22

Though God's people will be surrounded by enemies who are bent upon their destruction, yet the anguish which they suffer is not a dread of persecution for the truth's sake; they fear that every sin has not been repented of, and that through some fault in themselves they will fail to realize the fulfillment of the Saviour's promise: I "will keep thee from the hour of temptation, which shall come upon all the world." Revelation 3:10. If they could have the assurance of pardon they would not shrink from torture or death; but should they prove unworthy, and lose their lives because of their own defects of character, then God's holy name would be reproached.

They afflict their souls before God, pointing to their past repentance of their many sins, and pleading the Saviour's promise: "Let him take hold of My strength, that he may make peace with Me; and he shall make peace with Me." Isaiah 27:5. Their faith does not fail because their prayers are not immediately answered. Though suffering the keenest anxiety, terror, and distress, they do not cease their intercessions. They lay hold of the strength of God as Jacob laid hold of the Angel; and the language of their souls is: "I will not let Thee go, except Thou bless me."

(12) HOW WILL GOD REGARD THE PRAYERS OF THOSE WHO CONTINUE TO NEGLECT HIS LAWS AND LIVE WITH UNCONFESSED SINS?

____

____

____

Proverbs 28:9; 1 Thessalonians 4:8

Had not Jacob previously repented of his sin in obtaining the birthright by fraud, God would not have heard his prayer and mercifully preserved his life. So, in the time of trouble, if the people of God had unconfessed sins to appear before them while tortured with fear and anguish, they would be overwhelmed; despair would cut off their faith, and they could not have confidence to plead with God for deliverance. But while they have a deep sense of their unworthiness, they have no concealed wrongs to reveal. Their sins have gone beforehand to judgment and have been blotted out, and they cannot bring them to remembrance.

(13) HOW DOES GOD REWARD THOSE WHO HAVE BEEN FAITHFUL IN SMALL THINGS?

____

____

Matthew 25:21

Satan leads many to believe that God will overlook their unfaithfulness in the minor affairs of life; but the Lord shows in His dealings with Jacob that He will in no wise sanction or tolerate evil. All who endeavor to excuse or conceal their sins, and permit them to remain upon the books of heaven, unconfessed and unforgiven, will be overcome by Satan. The more exalted their profession and the more honorable the position which they hold, the more grievous is their course in the sight of God and the more sure the triumph of their great adversary. Those who delay a preparation for the day of God cannot obtain it in the time of trouble or at any subsequent time. The case of all such is hopeless.

(14) WHAT IS THE FRUIT OF TRUE REPENTANCE?

____

____

Psalm 38:18; Ezekiel 36:31

Those professed Christians who come up to that last fearful conflict unprepared will, in their despair, confess their sins in words of burning anguish, while the wicked exult over their distress. These confessions are of the same character as was that of Esau or of Judas. Those who make them, lament the result of transgression, but not its guilt. They feel no true contrition, no abhorrence of evil. They acknowledge their sin, through fear of punishment; but, like Pharaoh of old, they would return to their defiance of Heaven should the judgments be removed.

(15) IF WE HAVE RETURNED TO THE LORD IN TRUE REPENTANCE, WHAT WILL BE THE RESULT OF THE FIRE OF AFFLICTION?

____

____

____

Job 23:10; 1 Peter 1:7; Isaiah 13:12

Jacob's history is also an assurance that God will not cast off those who have been deceived and tempted and betrayed into sin, but who have returned unto Him with true repentance. While Satan seeks to destroy this class, God will send His angels to comfort and protect them in the time of peril. The assaults of Satan are fierce and determined, his delusions are terrible; but the Lord's eye is upon His people, and His ear listens to their cries. Their affliction is great, the flames of the furnace seem about to consume them; but the Refiner will bring them forth as gold tried in the fire. God's love for His children during the period of their severest trial is as strong and tender as in the days of their sunniest prosperity; but it is needful for them to be placed in the furnace of fire; their earthliness must be consumed, that the image of Christ may be perfectly reflected.

(16) WHAT TYPE OF PRAYERS AVAIL MUCH?

____

____

James 5:16

The season of distress and anguish before us will require a faith that can endure weariness, delay, and hunger—a faith that will not faint though severely tried. The period of probation is granted to all to prepare for that time. Jacob prevailed because he was persevering and determined. His victory is an evidence of the power of importunate prayer. All who will lay hold of God's promises, as he did, and be as earnest and persevering as he was, will succeed as he succeeded. Those who are unwilling to deny self, to agonize before God, to pray long and earnestly for His blessing, will not obtain it. Wrestling with God—how few know what it is! How few have ever had their souls drawn out after God with intensity of desire until every power is on the stretch. When waves of despair which no language can express sweep over the suppliant, how few cling with unyielding faith to the promises of God.

(17) WHAT IS THE LIFELINE OF THE TRUE CHRISTIAN, BOTH NOW AND IN THE PERILOUS TIMES TO COME?

____

____

____

Romans 1:17; Galations 3:11

Those who exercise but little faith now, are in the greatest danger of falling under the power of satanic delusions and the decree to compel the conscience. And even if they endure the test they will be plunged into deeper distress and anguish in the time of trouble, because they have never made it a habit to trust in God. The lessons of faith which they have neglected they will be forced to learn under a terrible pressure of discouragement.

(18) WHAT IS THE KEY TO MAINTAINING OUR LIFELINE OF FAITH?

____

____

____

____

1 Thessalonians 5:17

We should now acquaint ourselves with God by proving His promises. Angels record every prayer that is earnest and sincere. We should rather dispense with selfish gratifications than neglect communion with God. The deepest poverty, the greatest self-denial, with His approval, is better than riches, honors, ease, and friendship without it. We must take time to pray. If we allow our minds to be absorbed by worldly interests, the Lord may give us time by removing from us our idols of gold, of houses, or of fertile lands.

(19) WHY CAN WE NOT RELY ON FAMILY, FRIENDS, OR OUR RELIGIOUS LEADERS TO MAINTAIN OUR SPIRITUAL LIFELINE?

____

____

____

Philippians 2:12

The "time of trouble, such as never was," is soon to open upon us; and we shall need an experience which we do not now possess and which many are too indolent to obtain. It is often the case that trouble is greater in anticipation than in reality; but this is not true of the crisis before us. The most vivid presentation cannot reach the magnitude of the ordeal. In that time of trial, every soul must stand for himself before God. "Though Noah, Daniel, and Job" were in the land, "as I live, saith the Lord God, they shall deliver neither son nor daughter; they shall but deliver their own souls by their righteousness." Ezekiel 14:20.

(20) IF WE UNITE OUR WEAKNESS WITH GOD'S STRENGTH, WHAT TYPE OF NATURE IS POSSIBLE FOR US TO OBTAIN?

____

____

____

2 Peter 1:4

It is in this life that we are to separate sin from us, through faith in the atoning blood of Christ. Our precious Saviour invites us to join ourselves to Him, to unite our weakness to His strength, our ignorance to His wisdom, our unworthiness to His merits. God's providence is the school in which we are to learn the meekness and lowliness of Jesus. The Lord is ever setting before us, not the way we would choose, which seems easier and pleasanter to us, but the true aims of life. It rests with us to cooperate with the agencies which Heaven employs in the work of conforming our characters to the divine model. None can neglect or defer this work but at the most fearful peril to their souls.

(21) WHAT THREE STRATEGIES WILL SATAN AND HIS EVIL AGENTS EMPLOY TO DECEIVE THE MULTITUDES?

____

____

____

2 Thessalonians 2:9

Fearful sights of a supernatural character will soon be revealed in the heavens, in token of the power of miracle-working demons. The spirits of devils will go forth to the kings of the earth and to the whole world, to fasten them in deception, and urge them on to unite with Satan in his last struggle against the government of heaven. By these agencies, rulers and subjects will be alike deceived. Persons will arise pretending to be Christ Himself, and claiming the title and worship which belong to the world's Redeemer. They will perform wonderful miracles of healing and will profess to have revelations from heaven contradicting the testimony of the Scriptures.

(22) WHAT WILL BE THE CROWNING ACT OF DECEPTION?

____

____

____

____

Matthew 24:24

As the crowning act in the great drama of deception, Satan himself will personate Christ. The church has long professed to look to the Saviour's advent as the consummation of her hopes. Now the great deceiver will make it appear that Christ has come. In different parts of the earth, Satan will manifest himself among men as a majestic being of dazzling brightness, resembling the description of the Son of God given by John in the Revelation 1:13-15. The glory that surrounds him is unsurpassed by anything that mortal eyes have yet beheld. The shout of triumph rings out upon the air: "Christ has come! Christ has come!" The people prostrate themselves in adoration before him, while he lifts up his hands and pronounces a blessing upon them, as Christ blessed His disciples when He was upon the earth. His voice is soft and subdued, yet full of melody. In gentle, compassionate tones he presents some of the same gracious, heavenly truths which the Saviour uttered; he heals the diseases of the people, and then, in his assumed character of Christ, he claims to have changed the Sabbath to Sunday, and commands all to hallow the day which he has blessed. He declares that those who persist in keeping holy the seventh day are blaspheming his name by refusing to listen to his angels sent to them with light and truth. This is the strong, almost overmastering delusion. Like the Samaritans who were deceived by Simon Magus, the multitudes, from the least to the greatest, give heed to these sorceries, saying: This is "the great power of God." Acts 8:10.

(23) WHAT WILL PREVENT GOD'S PEOPLE FROM BEING DECEIVED?

____

____

____

____

____

Isaiah 8:20

But the people of God will not be misled. The teachings of this false Christ are not in accordance with the Scriptures. His blessing is pronounced upon the worshipers of the beast and his image, the very class upon whom the Bible declares that God's unmingled wrath shall be poured out.

(24) IN WHAT MANNER WILL THE TRUE CHRIST RETURN?

____

____

____

____

Matthew 24:30,31

Satan is not permitted to counterfeit the manner of Christ's advent. The Saviour has warned His people against deception upon this point, and has clearly foretold the manner of His second coming. "There shall arise false christs, and false prophets, and shall show great signs and wonders; insomuch that, if it were possible, they shall deceive the very elect. . . . Wherefore if they shall say unto you, Behold, He is in the desert; go not forth; behold, He is in the secret chambers; believe it not. For as the lightning cometh out of the east, and shineth even unto the west; so shall also the coming of the Son of man be." Matthew 24:24-27, 31; 25:31; Revelation 1:7; 1 Thessalonians 4:16, 17. This coming there is no possibility of counterfeiting. It will be universally known—witnessed by the whole world.

(25) WHY WILL THE MAJORITY BE DECEIVED?

____

____

____

2 Thessalonians 2:10

Only those who have been diligent students of the Scriptures and who have received the love of the truth will be shielded from the powerful delusion that takes the world captive. By the Bible testimony these will detect the deceiver in his disguise.

(26) WHAT THREE SNARES ARE WE WARNED TO AVOID?

____

____

____

1 John 2:16

To all the testing time will come. By the sifting of temptation the genuine Christian will be revealed. Are the people of God now so firmly established upon His word that they would not yield to the evidence of their senses? Would they, in such a crisis, cling to the Bible and the Bible only? Satan will, if possible, prevent them from obtaining a preparation to stand in that day. He will so arrange affairs as to hedge up their way, entangle them with earthly treasures, cause them to carry a heavy, wearisome burden, that their hearts may be overcharged with the cares of this life and the day of trial may come upon them as a thief.

(27) WHERE WILL MANY OF GOD'S FAITHFUL SEEK REFUGE IN THIS GREAT TIME OF TROUBLE?

____

____

Isaiah 33:16

As the decree issued by the various rulers of Christendom against commandment keepers shall withdraw the protection of government and abandon them to those who desire their destruction, the people of God will flee from the cities and villages and associate together in companies, dwelling in the most desolate and solitary places. Many will find refuge in the strongholds of the mountains. Like the Christians of the Piedmont valleys, they will make the high places of the earth their sanctuaries and will thank God for "the munitions of rocks."

(28) AS MANY SUFFER IMPRISONMENT FOR THEIR FAITH, WHAT PROMISE MAY THEY CLAIM?

____

____

____

____

Isaiah 49:15,16; 44:21; 1 Samuel 2:30

But many of all nations and of all classes, high and low, rich and poor, black and white, will be cast into the most unjust and cruel bondage. The beloved of God pass weary days, bound in chains, shut in by prison bars, sentenced to be slain, some apparently left to die of starvation in dark and loathsome dungeons. No human ear is open to hear their moans; no human hand is ready to lend them help.

Will the Lord forget His people in this trying hour? Did He forget faithful Noah when judgments were visited upon the antediluvian world? Did He forget Lot when the fire came down from heaven to consume the cities of the plain? Did He forget Joseph surrounded by idolaters in Egypt? Did He forget Elijah when the oath of Jezebel threatened him with the fate of the prophets of Baal? Did He forget Jeremiah in the dark and dismal pit of his prison house? Did He forget the three worthies in the fiery furnace? or Daniel in the den of lions?

Though enemies may thrust them into prison, yet dungeon walls cannot cut off the communication between their souls and Christ. One who sees their every weakness, who is acquainted with every trial, is above all earthly powers; and angels will come to them in lonely cells, bringing light and peace from heaven. The prison will be as a palace; for the rich in faith dwell there, and the gloomy walls will be lighted up with heavenly light as when Paul and Silas prayed and sang praises at midnight in the Philippian dungeon.

(29) HOW DOES THIS VERSE DESCRIBE THE ACT OF GOD DELIVERING JUDGMENT ON THE WICKED?

____

____

____

Isaiah 28:21

God's judgments will be visited upon those who are seeking to oppress and destroy His people. His long forbearance with the wicked emboldens men in transgression, but their punishment is nonetheless certain and terrible because it is long delayed. . . . To our merciful God the act of punishment is a strange act. "As I live, saith the Lord God, I have no pleasure in the death of the wicked." Ezekiel 33:11. The Lord is "merciful and gracious, long-suffering, and abundant in goodness and truth, . . . forgiving iniquity and transgression and sin." Yet He will "by no means clear the guilty." The Lord is slow to anger, and great in power, and will not at all acquit the wicked." Exodus 34:6, 7; Nahum 1:3. By terrible things in righteousness He will vindicate the authority of His downtrodden law. The severity of the retribution awaiting the transgressor may be judged by the Lord's reluctance to execute justice. The nation with which He bears long, and which He will not smite until it has filled up the measure of its iniquity in God's account, will finally drink the cup of wrath unmixed with mercy.

(30) WHAT SEVEN DREADFUL PLAGUES OF JUDGMENT WILL

THOSE POSSESSING THE MARK OF DISOBEDIENCE EXPERIENCE?

____

____

____

____

____

____

____

Revelation 16:2,3,4,8,10,12,18

When Christ ceases His intercession in the sanctuary, the unmingled wrath threatened against those who worship the beast and his image and receive his mark (Revelation 14:9, 10), will be poured out. The plagues upon Egypt when God was about to deliver Israel were similar in character to those more terrible and extensive judgments which are to fall upon the world just before the final deliverance of God's people. . . . Terrible as these inflictions are, God's justice stands fully vindicated. The angel of God declares: "Thou art righteous, O Lord, . . . because Thou hast judged thus. For they have shed the blood of saints and prophets, and Thou hast given them blood to drink; for they are worthy." Revelation 16:2-6. By condemning the people of God to death, they have as truly incurred the guilt of their blood as if it had been shed by their hands. In like manner Christ declared the Jews of His time guilty of all the blood of holy men which had been shed since the days of Abel; for they possessed the same spirit and were seeking to do the same work with these murderers of the prophets.

These plagues are not universal, or the inhabitants of the earth would be wholly cut off. Yet they will be the most awful scourges that have ever been known to mortals. All the judgments upon men, prior to the close of probation, have been mingled with mercy. The pleading blood of Christ has shielded the sinner from receiving the full measure of his guilt; but in the final judgment, wrath is poured out unmixed with mercy.

(31) WHEN THE WICKED ARE SUFFERING FROM HUNGER WHAT WILL SUSTAIN THE FAITHFUL?

____

____

Isaiah 33:15,16; 41:17; Isaiah 51:23

The people of God will not be free from suffering; but while persecuted and distressed, while they endure privation and suffer for want of food they will not be left to perish. That God who cared for Elijah will not pass by one of His self-sacrificing children. He who numbers the hairs of their head will care for them, and in time of famine they shall be satisfied. While the wicked are dying from hunger and pestilence, angels will shield the righteous and supply their wants. To him that "walketh righteously" is the promise: "Bread shall be given him; his waters shall be sure."

(32) WHEN ALL HOPE APPEARS LOST, LIKE JACOB IN HIS TIME OF TROUBLE, WHAT WILL BE THE PLEA OF THE RIGHTEOUS?

____

____

____

Genesis 32:26

Yet to human sight it will appear that the people of God must soon seal their testimony with their blood as did the martyrs before them. They themselves begin to fear that the Lord has left them to fall by the hand of their enemies. It is a time of fearful agony. Day and night they cry unto God for deliverance. The wicked exult, and the jeering cry is heard: "Where now is your faith? Why does not God deliver you out of our hands if you are indeed His people?" But the waiting ones remember Jesus dying upon Calvary's cross and the chief priests and rulers shouting in mockery: "He saved others; Himself He cannot save. If He be the King of Israel, let Him now come down from the cross, and we will believe Him." Matthew 27:42. Like Jacob, all are wrestling with God. Their countenances express their internal struggle. Paleness sits upon every face. Yet they cease not their earnest intercession.

(33) WHO HAS GOD COMMISSIONED FOR THE PROTECTION OF HIS FAITHFUL?

____

____

____

Psalms 34:7; Psalm 91:11

Could men see with heavenly vision, they would behold companies of angels that excel in strength stationed about those who have kept the word of Christ's patience. With sympathizing tenderness, angels have witnessed their distress and have heard their prayers. They are waiting the word of their Commander to snatch them from their peril. But they must wait yet a little longer. The people of God must drink of the cup and be baptized with the baptism. The very delay, so painful to them, is the best answer to their petitions. As they endeavor to wait trustingly for the Lord to work they are led to exercise faith, hope, and patience, which have been too little exercised during their religious experience. Yet for the elect's sake the time of trouble will be shortened. "Shall not God avenge His own elect, which cry day and night unto Him? . . . I tell you that He will avenge them speedily." Luke 18:7, 8. The end will come more quickly than men expect. The wheat will be gathered and bound in sheaves for the garner of God; the tares will be bound as fagots for the fires of destruction.

(34) AT THE COMMAND OF THE FATHER, WHAT WONDERFUL PROPHECY OF PROMISE WILL BE FULFILLED?

____

____

____

Psalm 91:3-8

The heavenly sentinels, faithful to their trust, continue their watch. Though a general decree has fixed the time when commandment keepers may be put to death, their enemies will in some cases anticipate the decree, and before the time specified, will endeavor to take their lives. But none can pass the mighty guardians stationed about every faithful soul. Some are assailed in their flight from the cities and villages; but the swords raised against them break and fall powerless as a straw. Others are defended by angels in the form of men of war.

The eye of God, looking down the ages, was fixed upon the crisis which His people are to meet, when earthly powers shall be arrayed against them. Like the captive exile, they will be in fear of death by starvation or by violence. But the Holy One who divided the Red Sea before Israel, will manifest His mighty power and turn their captivity. "They shall be Mine, saith the Lord of hosts, in that day when I make up My jewels; and I will spare them, as a man spareth his own son that serveth him." Malachi 3:17. If the blood of Christ's faithful witnesses were shed at this time, it would not, like the blood of the martyrs, be as seed sown to yield a harvest for God. Their fidelity would not be a testimony to convince others of the truth; for the obdurate heart has beaten back the waves of mercy until they return no more. If the righteous were now left to fall a prey to their enemies, it would be a triumph for the prince of darkness. Says the psalmist: "In the time of trouble He shall hide me in His pavilion: in the secret of His tabernacle shall He hide me." Psalm 27:5. Christ has spoken: "Come, My people, enter thou into thy chambers, and shut thy doors about thee: hide thyself as it were for a little moment, until the indignation be overpast. For, behold, the Lord cometh out of His place to punish the inhabitants of the earth for their iniquity." Isaiah 26:20, 21. Glorious will be the deliverance of those who have patiently waited for His coming and whose names are written in the book of life.

I love the Lord with all my heart. I pray that I am counted on His side when He proclaims, "He that is righteous let him be righteous still."

Circle: Yes Undecided

I now realize that Satan is, like a roaring lion, seeking whom he may devour. I pray for wisdom to continue to study and accept God's Word to avoid the deceptions that Satan will manifest in the final moments of this world's history.

Circle: Yes Undecided

I am grateful to God for warning us of the great "time of trouble" that will come to those who honor His divine precepts.

Circle: Yes Undecided

I pray that God will refine my character and strengthen my faith so, by His grace, I can overcome for His glory.

Circle: Yes Undecided

In love and faith, I trustfully give all into God's hands. I pray that by miraculous preservation of life or in a martyr's death, He will use me to glorify His name.

Circle: Yes Undecided

Study Notes: ______________________________

____

____

____

____

____

God's People Delivered - 11

When the protection of human laws shall be withdrawn from those who honor the law of God, there will be, in different lands, a simultaneous movement for their destruction. As the time appointed in the decree draws near, the people will conspire to root out the hated sect. It will be determined to strike in one night a decisive blow, which shall utterly silence the voice of dissent and reproof.

(1) WHAT PROMISE CAN THOSE WHO REMAIN FAITHFUL CLAIM?

____

____

____

Revelation 3:8-11

The people of God—some in prison cells, some hidden in solitary retreats in the forests and the mountains—still plead for divine protection, while in every quarter companies of armed men, urged on by hosts of evil angels, are preparing for the work of death. It is now, in the hour of utmost extremity, that the God of Israel will interpose for the deliverance of His chosen. Saith the Lord; "Ye shall have a song, as in the night when a holy solemnity is kept; and gladness of heart, as when one goeth . . . to come into the mountain of the Lord, to the Mighty One of Israel. And the Lord shall cause His glorious voice to be heard, and shall show the lighting down of His arm, with the indignation of His anger, and with the flame of a devouring fire, with scattering, and tempest, and hailstones." Isaiah 30:29, 30.

With shouts of triumph, jeering, and imprecation, throngs of evil men are about to rush upon their prey, when, lo, a dense blackness, deeper than the darkness of the night, falls upon the earth. Then a rainbow, shining with the glory from the throne of God, spans the heavens and seems to encircle each praying company. The angry multitudes are suddenly arrested. Their mocking cries die away. The objects of their murderous rage are forgotten. With fearful forebodings they gaze upon the symbol of God's covenant and long to be shielded from its overpowering brightness.

(2) WHAT WORDS OF JOY WILL SPRING FORTH FROM THE LIPS OF THE FAITHFUL?

____

____

____

Isaiah 25:9; Psalm 46:1-3

By the people of God a voice, clear and melodious, is heard, saying, "Look up," and lifting their eyes to the heavens, they behold the bow of promise. The black, angry clouds that covered the firmament are parted, and like Stephen they look up steadfastly into heaven and see the glory of God and the Son of man seated upon His throne. In His divine form they discern the marks of His humiliation; and from His lips they hear the request presented before His Father and the holy angels: "I will that they also, whom Thou hast given Me, be with Me where I am." John 17:24. Again a voice, musical and triumphant, is heard, saying: "They come! they come! holy, harmless, and undefiled. They have kept the word of My patience; they shall walk among the angels;" and the pale, quivering lips of those who have held fast their faith utter a shout of victory.

(3) WHAT WORDS COME FROM THE MOUTH OF GOD?

____

____

____

Revelation 16:17

It is at midnight that God manifests His power for the deliverance of His people. The sun appears, shining in its strength. Signs and wonders follow in quick succession. The wicked look with terror and amazement upon the scene, while the righteous behold with solemn joy the tokens of their deliverance. Everything in nature seems turned out of its course. The streams cease to flow. Dark, heavy clouds come up and clash against each other. In the midst of the angry heavens is one clear space of indescribable glory, whence comes the voice of God like the sound of many waters, saying: "It is done."

(4) WHAT GREAT EVENT WILL THE VOICE OF GOD CAUSE?

____

____

____

____

Revelation 16:18

That voice shakes the heavens and the earth . . . The firmament appears to open and shut. The glory from the throne of God seems flashing through. The mountains shake like a reed in the wind, and ragged rocks are scattered on every side. There is a roar as of a coming tempest. The sea is lashed into fury. There is heard the shriek of a hurricane like the voice of demons upon a mission of destruction. The whole earth heaves and swells like the waves of the sea. Its surface is breaking up. Its very foundations seem to be giving way. Mountain chains are sinking. Inhabited islands disappear. The seaports that have become like Sodom for wickedness are swallowed up by the angry waters. Babylon the great has come in remembrance before God, "to give unto her the cup of the wine of the fierceness of His wrath." Great hailstones, every one "about the weight of a talent," are doing their work of destruction. Verses 19, 21. The proudest cities of the earth are laid low. The lordly palaces, upon which the world's great men have lavished their wealth in order to glorify themselves, are crumbling to ruin before their eyes. Prison walls are rent asunder, and God's people, who have been held in bondage for their faith, are set free.

(5) WHO WILL WITNESS THE SECOND COMING OF CHRIST?

___

___

___

Revelation 1:7; Daniel 12:2; 2 Peter 3:10

Graves are opened, and "many of them that sleep in the dust of the earth . . . awake, some to everlasting life, and some to shame and everlasting contempt." All who have died in the faith of the third angel's message come forth from the tomb glorified, to hear God's covenant of peace with those who have kept His law. "They also which pierced Him" (Revelation 1:7), those that mocked and derided Christ's dying agonies, and the most violent opposers of His truth and His people, are raised to behold Him in His glory and to see the honor placed upon the loyal and obedient.

(6) WHAT WILL BE THE RESPONSE OF THE WICKED AS THEY REALIZE THEY ARE ABOUT TO WITNESS THE SECOND COMING OF CHRIST?

___

___

___

Revelation 6:16; Isaiah 2:10-12,20,21

Thick clouds still cover the sky; yet the sun now and then breaks through, appearing like the avenging eye of Jehovah. Fierce lightnings leap from the heavens, enveloping the earth in a sheet of flame. Above the terrific roar of thunder, voices, mysterious and awful, declare the doom of the wicked. The words spoken are not comprehended by all; but they are distinctly understood by the false teachers. Those who a little before were so reckless, so boastful and defiant, so exultant in their cruelty to God's commandment-keeping people, are now overwhelmed with consternation and shuddering in fear. Their wails are heard above the sound of the elements. Demons acknowledge the deity of Christ and tremble before His power, while men are supplicating for mercy and groveling in abject terror.

(7) WHAT SONG OF TRIUMPHAL RESPONSE WILL RESOUND FROM THE RIGHTEOUS?

___

___

___

___

___

Psalm 46:1-3

Through a rift in the clouds there beams a star whose brilliancy is increased fourfold in contrast with the darkness. It speaks hope and joy to the faithful, but severity and wrath to the transgressors of God's law. Those who have sacrificed all for Christ are now secure, hidden as in the secret of the Lord's pavilion. They have been tested, and before the world and the despisers of truth they have evinced their fidelity to Him who died for them. A marvelous change has come over those who have held fast their integrity in the very face of death. They have been suddenly delivered from the dark and terrible tyranny of men transformed to demons. Their faces, so lately pale, anxious, and haggard, are now aglow with wonder, faith, and love. Their voices rise in triumphant song . . .

(8) WHAT WILL BE DECLARED IN THE HEAVENS?

____

____

____

Psalm 50:6

While these words of holy trust ascend to God, the clouds sweep back, and the starry heavens are seen, unspeakably glorious in contrast with the black and angry firmament on either side. The glory of the celestial city streams from the gates ajar. Then there appears against the sky a hand holding two tables of stone folded together. Says the prophet: "The heavens shall declare His righteousness: for God is judge Himself." . . . That holy law, God's righteousness, that amid thunder and flame was proclaimed from Sinai as the guide of life, is now revealed to men as the rule of judgment. The hand opens the tables, and there are seen the precepts of the Decalogue, traced as with a pen of fire. The words are so plain that all can read them. Memory is aroused, the darkness of superstition and heresy is swept from every mind, and God's ten words, brief, comprehensive, and authoritative, are presented to the view of all the inhabitants of the earth.

(9) WHAT TRUTH CONCERNING GOD'S COMMANDMENTS WILL STRIKE TERROR IN THE HEARTS OF THE WICKED?

____

____

____

Psalm 119:160; Isaiah 40:8; Matthew 5:18

It is impossible to describe the horror and despair of those who have trampled upon God's holy requirements. The Lord gave them His law; they might have compared their characters with it and learned their defects while there was yet opportunity for repentance and reform; but in order to secure the favor of the world, they set aside its precepts and taught others to transgress. They have endeavored to compel God's people to profane His Sabbath. Now they are condemned by that law which they have despised. With awful distinctness they see that they are without excuse. They chose whom they would serve and worship. "Then shall ye return, and discern between the righteous and the wicked, between him that serveth God and him that serveth Him not." Malachi 3:18.

(10) WHAT IS THE RESULT OF KNOWING TRUTH AND NOT SHARING THIS KNOWLEDGE WITH THE LOST?

____

____

____

____

Ezekiel 3:18,19

The enemies of God's law, from the ministers down to the least among them, have a new conception of truth and duty. Too late they see that the Sabbath of the fourth commandment is the seal of the living God. Too late they see the true nature of their spurious sabbath and the sandy foundation upon which they have been building. They find that they have been fighting against God. Religious teachers have led souls to perdition while professing to guide them to the gates of Paradise. Not until the day of final accounts will it be known how great is the responsibility of men in holy office and how terrible are the results of their unfaithfulness. Only in eternity can we rightly estimate the loss of a single soul. Fearful will be the doom of him to whom God shall say: Depart, thou wicked servant.

(11) WHERE WILL CHRIST BE SEEN AT HIS COMING?

____

____

____

Matthew 26:64

Soon there appears in the east a small black cloud, about half the size of a man's hand. It is the cloud which surrounds the Saviour and which seems in the distance to be shrouded in darkness. The people of God know this to be the sign of the Son of man. In solemn silence they gaze upon it as it draws nearer the earth, becoming lighter and more glorious, until it is a great white cloud, its base a glory like consuming fire, and above it the rainbow of the covenant. Jesus rides forth as a mighty conqueror. Not now a "Man of Sorrows," to drink the bitter cup of shame and woe, He comes, victor in heaven and earth, to judge the living and the dead. "Faithful and True," "in righteousness He doth judge and make war." And "the armies which were in heaven" (Revelation 19:11, 14) follow Him. With anthems of celestial melody the holy angels, a vast, unnumbered throng, attend Him on His way. The firmament seems filled with radiant forms—"ten thousand times ten thousand, and thousands of thousands."

(12) HOW DOES THE PROPHET HABAKKUK DESCRIBE THE SECOND COMING OF CHRIST?

____

____

____

Habakkuk 3:3,4

No human pen can portray the scene; no mortal mind is adequate to conceive its splendor. . . . As the living cloud comes still nearer, every eye beholds the Prince of life. No crown of thorns now mars that sacred head; but a diadem of glory rests on His holy brow. His countenance outshines the dazzling brightness of the noonday sun. "And He hath on His vesture and on His thigh a name written, King of kings, and Lord of lords." Revelation 19:16.

(13) HOW DOES THE PROPHET JEREMIAH DESCRIBE THE REACTION OF HUMANITY TO THIS GREAT EVENT?

____

____

____

____

Jeremiah 30:6,7

Before His presence "all faces are turned into paleness;" upon the rejecters of God's mercy falls the terror of eternal despair. "The heart melteth, and the knees smite together, . . . and the faces of them all gather blackness." Jeremiah 30:6; Nahum 2:10. The righteous cry with trembling: "Who shall be able to stand?" The angels' song is hushed, and there is a period of awful silence. Then the voice of Jesus is heard, saying: "My grace is sufficient for you." The faces of the righteous are lighted up, and joy fills every heart. And the angels strike a note higher and sing again as they draw still nearer to the earth.

(14) WHAT PROPHECY GIVEN BY CHRIST INVOLVING THOSE RESPONSIBLE FOR HIS CRUCIFICTION WILL BE FULFILLED?

____

____

____

____

____

Matthew 26:64; Revelation 1:7

There are those who mocked Christ in His humiliation. With thrilling power come to their minds the Sufferer's words, when, adjured by the high priest, He solemnly declared: "Hereafter shall ye see the Son of man sitting on the right hand of power, and coming in the clouds of heaven." Now they behold Him in His glory, and they are yet to see Him sitting on the right hand of power.

Those who derided His claim to be the Son of God are speechless now. There is the haughty Herod who jeered at His royal title and bade the mocking soldiers crown Him king. There are the very men who with impious hands placed upon His form the purple robe, upon His sacred brow the thorny crown, and in His unresisting hand the mimic scepter, and bowed before Him in blasphemous mockery. The men who smote and spit upon the Prince of life now turn from His piercing gaze and seek to flee from the overpowering glory of His presence. Those who drove the nails through His hands and feet, the soldier who pierced His side, behold these marks with terror and remorse.

In the lives of all who reject truth there are moments when conscience awakens, when memory presents the torturing recollection of a life of hypocrisy and the soul is harassed with vain regrets. But what are these compared with the remorse of that day when "fear cometh as desolation," when "destruction cometh as a whirlwind"! Proverbs 1:27. Those who would have destroyed Christ and His faithful people now witness the glory which rests upon them. In the midst of their terror they hear the voices of the saints in joyful strains exclaiming: "Lo, this is our God; we have waited for Him, and He will save us." Isaiah 25:9.

(15) WHAT CRY WILL FILL THE HEAVENS AS CHRIST CALLS THE RIGHTEOUS DEAD TO LIFE?

____

____

____

1 Corinthians 15:55

Amid the reeling of the earth, the flash of lightning, and the roar of thunder, the voice of the Son of God calls forth the sleeping saints. He looks upon the graves of the righteous, then, raising His hands to heaven, He cries: "Awake, awake, awake, ye that sleep in the dust, and arise!" Throughout the length and breadth of the earth the dead shall hear that voice, and they that hear shall live. And the whole earth shall ring with the tread of the exceeding great army of every nation, kindred, tongue, and people. From the prison house of death they come, clothed with immortal glory, crying: "O death, where is thy sting? O grave, where is thy victory?" And the living righteous and the risen saints unite their voices in a long, glad shout of victory.

(16) WHAT CHANGE WILL OCCUR IN THE RIGHTEOUS?

___

___

___

___

1 Corinthians 15:52,53

All come forth from their graves the same in stature as when they entered the tomb. Adam, who stands among the risen throng, is of lofty height and majestic form, in stature but little below the Son of God. He presents a marked contrast to the people of later generations; in this one respect is shown the great degeneracy of the race. But all arise with the freshness and vigor of eternal youth. In the beginning, man was created in the likeness of God, not only in character, but in form and feature. Sin defaced and almost obliterated the divine image; but Christ came to restore that which had been lost. He will change our vile bodies and fashion them like unto His glorious body. The mortal, corruptible form, devoid of comeliness, once polluted with sin, becomes perfect, beautiful, and immortal. All blemishes and deformities are left in the grave. Restored to the tree of life in the long-lost Eden, the redeemed will "grow up" (Malachi 4:2) to the full stature of the race in its primeval glory. The last lingering traces of the curse of sin will be removed, and Christ's faithful ones will appear in "the beauty of the Lord our God," in mind and soul and body reflecting the perfect image of their Lord. Oh, wonderful redemption! long talked of, long hoped for, contemplated with eager anticipation, but never fully understood.

(17) WHERE WILL THE ELECT GO IMMEDIATELY FOLLOWING THIS CHANGE?

___

___

___

___

1 Thessalonians 4:17

The living righteous are changed "in a moment, in the twinkling of an eye." At the voice of God they were glorified; now they are made immortal and with the risen saints are caught up to meet their Lord in the air. Angels "gather together His elect from the four winds, from one end of heaven to the other." Little children are borne by holy angels to their mothers' arms. Friends long separated by death are united, nevermore to part, and with songs of gladness ascend together to the City of God.

(18) WHAT WILL CHRIST OUR RIGHTEOUS JUDGE BESTOW ON EACH OF HIS REDEEMED?

___

___

___

1 Peter 5:4

Before entering the City of God, the Saviour bestows upon His followers the emblems of victory and invests them with the insignia of their royal state. The glittering ranks are drawn up in the form of a hollow square about their King, whose form rises in majesty high above saint and angel, whose countenance beams upon them full of benignant love. Throughout the unnumbered host of the redeemed every glance is fixed upon Him, every eye beholds His glory whose "visage was so marred more than any man, and His form more than the sons of men." Upon the heads of the overcomers, Jesus with His own right hand places the crown of glory. For each there is a crown, bearing his own "new name" (Revelation 2:17), and the inscription, "Holiness to the Lord." In every hand are placed the victor's palm and the shining harp. Then, as the commanding angels strike the note, every hand sweeps the harp strings with skillful touch, awaking sweet music in rich, melodious strains. Rapture unutterable thrills every heart, and each voice is raised in grateful praise: "Unto Him that loved us, and washed us from our sins in His own blood, and hath made us kings and priests unto God and His Father; to Him be glory and dominion for ever and ever." Revelation 1:5, 6.

(19) WHAT JOYOUS INVITATION WILL CHRIST EXTEND TO HIS REDEEMED?

____

____

____

____

____

Matthew 25:34

Before the ransomed throng is the Holy City. Jesus opens wide the pearly gates, and the nations that have kept the truth enter in. There they behold the Paradise of God, the home of Adam in his innocency. Then that voice, richer than any music that ever fell on mortal ear, is heard, saying: "Your conflict is ended." "Come, ye blessed of My Father, inherit the kingdom prepared for you from the foundation of the world."

Now is fulfilled the Saviour's prayer for His disciples: "I will that they also, whom Thou hast given Me, be with Me where I am." "Faultless before the presence of His glory with exceeding joy" (Jude 24), Christ presents to the Father the purchase of His blood, declaring: "Here am I, and the children whom Thou hast given Me." "Those that Thou gavest Me I have kept." Oh, the wonders of redeeming love! the rapture of that hour when the infinite Father, looking upon the ransomed, shall behold His image, sin's discord banished, its blight removed, and the human once more in harmony with the divine!

With unutterable love, Jesus welcomes His faithful ones to the joy of their Lord. The Saviour's joy is in seeing, in the kingdom of glory, the souls that have been saved by His agony and humiliation. And the redeemed will be sharers in His joy, as they behold, among the blessed, those who have been won to Christ through their prayers, their labors, and their loving sacrifice. As they gather about the great white throne, gladness unspeakable will fill their hearts, when they behold those whom they have won for Christ, and see that one has gained others, and these still others, all brought into the haven of rest, there to lay their crowns at Jesus' feet and praise Him through the endless cycles of eternity.

(20) WHAT GROUP WILL BE PRIVILEGED TO SING A UNIQUE SONG OF PRAISE TO THEIR REDEEMER?

____

____

____

Revelation 14:3

Upon the crystal sea before the throne, that sea of glass as it were mingled with fire,—so resplendent is it with the glory of God,—are gathered the company that have "gotten the victory over the beast, and over his image, and over his mark, and over the number of his name." With the Lamb upon Mount Zion, "having the harps of God," they stand, the hundred and forty and four thousand that were redeemed from among men; and there is heard, as the sound of many waters, and as the sound of a great thunder, "the voice of harpers harping with their harps." And they sing "a new song" before the throne, a song which no man can learn save the hundred and forty and four thousand. It is the song of Moses and the Lamb—a song of deliverance. None but the hundred and forty-four thousand can learn that song; for it is the song of their experience—an experience such as no other company have ever had. "These are they which follow the Lamb whithersoever He goeth." These, having been translated from the earth, from among the living, are counted as "the first fruits unto God and to the Lamb." Revelation 15:2, 3; 14:1-5.

(21) WHAT DISTINGUISHES THIS GROUP FROM THE MULTITUDE OF THE REDEEMED?

____

____

____

Revelation 7:13,14

____

____

____

Revelation 14:4

"These are they which came out of great tribulation;" they have passed through the time of trouble such as never was since there was a nation; they have endured the anguish of the time of Jacob's trouble; they have stood without an intercessor through the final outpouring of God's judgments. But they have been delivered, for they have "washed their robes, and made them white in the blood of the Lamb." "In their mouth was found no guile: for they are without fault" before God. "Therefore are they before the throne of God, and serve Him day and night in His temple: and He that sitteth on the throne shall dwell among them." They have seen the earth wasted with famine and pestilence, the sun having power to scorch men with great heat, and they themselves have endured suffering, hunger, and thirst. But "they shall hunger no more, neither thirst any more; neither shall the sun light on them, nor any heat. For the Lamb which is in the midst of the throne shall feed them, and shall lead them unto living fountains of waters: and God shall wipe away all tears from their eyes." Revelation 7:14-17.

(22) WHAT PRINCIPLE WILL INSPIRE THE REDEEMED TO SHARE THEIR TESTIMONY THROUGHOUT THE UNIVERSE?

____

____

____

____

____

Luke 7:42,43

In all ages the Saviour's chosen have been educated and disciplined in the school of trial. They walked in narrow paths on earth; they were purified in the furnace of affliction. For Jesus' sake they endured opposition, hatred, calumny. They followed Him through conflicts sore; they endured self-denial and experienced bitter disappointments. By their own painful experience they learned the evil of sin, its power, its guilt, its woe; and they look upon it with abhorrence. A sense of the infinite sacrifice made for its cure humbles them in their own sight and fills their hearts with gratitude and praise which those who have never fallen cannot appreciate. They love much because they have been forgiven much. Having been partakers of Christ's sufferings, they are fitted to be partakers with Him of His glory.

(23) WHAT WILL BE REMOVED FROM THE RIGHTEOUS?

____

____

____

Isaiah 25:8

The heirs of God have come from garrets, from hovels, from dungeons, from scaffolds, from mountains, from deserts, from the caves of the earth, from the caverns of the sea. On earth they were "destitute, afflicted, tormented." Millions went down to the grave loaded with infamy because they steadfastly refused to yield to the deceptive claims of Satan. By human tribunals they were adjudged the vilest of criminals. But now "God is judge Himself." Psalm 50:6. Now the decisions of earth are reversed. "The rebuke of His people shall He take away." Isaiah 25:8. "They shall call them, The holy people, The redeemed of the Lord." He hath appointed "to give unto them beauty for ashes, the oil of joy for mourning, the garment of praise for the spirit of heaviness." Isaiah 62:12; 61:3. They are no longer feeble, afflicted, scattered, and oppressed. Henceforth they are to be ever with the Lord. They stand before the throne clad in richer robes than the most honored of the earth have ever worn. They are crowned with diadems more glorious than were ever placed upon the brow of earthly monarchs. The days of pain and weeping are forever ended. The King of glory has wiped the tears from all faces; every cause of grief has been removed. Amid the waving of palm branches they pour forth a song of praise, clear, sweet, and harmonious; every voice takes up the strain, until the anthem swells through the vaults of heaven: "Salvation to our God which sitteth upon the throne, and unto the Lamb." And all the inhabitants of heaven respond in the ascription: "Amen: Blessing, and glory, and wisdom, and thanksgiving, and honor, and power, and might, be unto our God for ever and ever." Revelation 7:10, 12.

(24) HOW DOES THE BIBLE DESCRIBE THE PLAN OF REDEMPTION?

____

____

____

1 Timothy 3:16; Ephesians 6:19

In this life we can only begin to understand the wonderful theme of redemption. With our finite comprehension we may consider most earnestly the shame and the glory, the life and the death, the justice and the mercy, that meet in the cross; yet with the utmost stretch of our mental powers we fail to grasp its full significance. The length and the breadth, the depth and the height, of redeeming love are but dimly comprehended. The plan of redemption will not be fully understood, even when the ransomed see as they are seen and know as they are known; but through the eternal ages new truth will continually unfold to the wondering and delighted mind. Though the griefs and pains and temptations of earth are ended and the cause removed, the people of God will ever have a distinct, intelligent knowledge of what their salvation has cost.

(25) WHAT IS THE PAST, PRESENT, AND FUTURE SCIENCE AND SONG OF THE REDEEMED?

____

____

____

Ephesians 3:18,19;1 Corinthians 1:17,18; Matthew ll:29; Romans 11:33

The cross of Christ will be the science and the song of the redeemed through all eternity. In Christ glorified they will behold Christ crucified. Never will it be forgotten that He whose power created and upheld the unnumbered worlds through the vast realms of space, the Beloved of God, the Majesty of heaven, He whom cherub and shining seraph delighted to adore—humbled Himself to uplift fallen man; that He bore the guilt and shame of sin, and the hiding of His Father's face, till the woes of a lost world broke His heart and crushed out His life on Calvary's cross. That the Maker of all worlds, the Arbiter of all destinies, should lay aside His glory and humiliate Himself from love to man will ever excite the wonder and adoration of the universe. As the nations of the saved look upon their Redeemer and behold the eternal glory of the Father shining in His countenance; as they behold His throne, which is from everlasting to everlasting, and know that His kingdom is to have no end, they break forth in rapturous song: "Worthy, worthy is the Lamb that was slain, and hath redeemed us to God by His own most precious blood!"

The mystery of the cross explains all other mysteries. In the light that streams from Calvary the attributes of God which had filled us with fear and awe appear beautiful and attractive. Mercy, tenderness, and parental love are seen to blend with holiness, justice, and power. While we behold the majesty of His throne, high and lifted up, we see His character in its gracious manifestations, and comprehend, as never before, the significance of that endearing title, "Our Father."

It will be seen that He who is infinite in wisdom could devise no plan for our salvation except the sacrifice of His Son. The compensation for this sacrifice is the joy of peopling the earth with ransomed beings, holy, happy, and immortal. The result of the Saviour's conflict with the powers of darkness is joy to the redeemed, redounding to the glory of God throughout eternity. And such is the value of the soul that the Father is satisfied with the price paid; and Christ Himself, beholding the fruits of His great sacrifice, is satisfied.

I am looking forward to that great day when Christ comes in the clouds of heaven to deliver His people from the wickedness of this earth and the terrible time of trouble that is before us.

Circle: Yes Undecided

I look forward with great anticipation to accept Christ's joyous invitation, "Come, ye blessed of my Father, inherit the kingdom prepared for you from the foundation of the world."

Circle: Yes Undecided

Desolation of the Earth - 12

(1) WHAT MESSAGE OF MERCY IS HEAVEN PROCLAIMING TO THOSE WHO ARE UNKNOWINGLY FOLLOWING THE FALSE DOCTRINES OF BABYLON?

____

____

____

Revelation 18:4; 14:8

(2) WHAT JUDGMENTS WILL BEFALL BABYLON AND THOSE WHO CLING TO HER TEACHINGS?

____

____

____

____

____

Revelation 18:8; Revelation 18:3-17

Such are the judgments that fall upon Babylon in the day of the visitation of God's wrath. She has filled up the measure of her iniquity; her time has come; she is ripe for destruction. When the voice of God turns the captivity of His people, there is a terrible awakening of those who have lost all in the great conflict of life. While probation continued they were blinded by Satan's deceptions, and they justified their course of sin. The rich prided themselves upon their superiority to those who were less favored; but they had obtained their riches by violation of the law of God.

(3) WHAT BASIC PRINCIPLE HAVE THOSE WHO PERISH WILLFULLY VIOLATED?

____

____

____

____

Matthew 25:43-45; Matthew 6:33; 2 Thessalonians 2:10

They had neglected to feed the hungry, to clothe the naked, to deal justly, and to love mercy. They had sought to exalt themselves and to obtain the homage of their fellow creatures. Now they are stripped of all that made them great and are left destitute and defenseless. They look with terror upon the destruction of the idols which they preferred before their Maker. They have sold their souls for earthly riches and enjoyments, and have not sought to become rich toward God. The result is, their lives are a failure; their pleasures are now turned to gall, their treasures to corruption. The gain of a lifetime is swept away in a moment. The rich bemoan the destruction of their grand houses, the scattering of their gold and silver. But their lamentations are silenced by the fear that they themselves are to perish with their idols.

(4) WHAT CHANGE OCCURS IN THE LIFE WHEN THE WICKED TRULY REPENT?

____

____

____

2 Chronicles 7:14; Isaiah 55:7

The wicked are filled with regret, not because of their sinful neglect of God and their fellow men, but because God has conquered. They lament that the result is what it is; but they do not repent of their wickedness. They would leave no means untried to conquer if they could.

(5) WHAT WONDERFUL PROMISE IS FULFILLED TO THE RIGHTEOUS?

____

____

____

____

____

____

____

____

Psalm 91:3-7

The world see the very class whom they have mocked and derided, and desired to exterminate, pass unharmed through pestilence, tempest, and earthquake. He who is to the transgressors of His law a devouring fire, is to His people a safe pavilion.

(6) WHAT JUDGMENT WILL BE PRONOUNCED UPON THE SPIRITUAL LEADERS WHO HAVE IGNORED TRUTH AND LEAD THEIR FLOCK ASTRAY?

____

____

____

Jeremiah 23:1,2; 25:34; Matthew 18:6

The minister who has sacrificed truth to gain the favor of men now discerns the character and influence of his teachings. It is apparent that the omniscient eye was following him as he stood in the desk, as he walked the streets, as he mingled with men in the various scenes of life. Every emotion of the soul, every line written, every word uttered, every act that led men to rest in a refuge of falsehood, has been scattering seed; and now, in the wretched, lost souls around him, he beholds the harvest.

(7) WHAT HAVE THESE UNFAITHFUL LEADERS FAILED TO ACKNOWLEDGE?

___

___

Psalm 119:160,142

Ministers and people see that they have not sustained the right relation to God. They see that they have rebelled against the Author of all just and righteous law. The setting aside of the divine precepts gave rise to thousands of springs of evil, discord, hatred, iniquity, until the earth became one vast field of strife, one sink of corruption. This is the view that now appears to those who rejected truth and chose to cherish error. No language can express the longing which the disobedient and disloyal feel for that which they have lost forever—eternal life. Men whom the world has worshiped for their talents and eloquence now see these things in their true light. They realize what they have forfeited by transgression, and they fall at the feet of those whose fidelity they have despised and derided, and confess that God has loved them.

(8) HOW WILL THE LOST REACT TOWARDS THOSE WHO HAVE BETRAYED THEM?

___

Zechariah 14:13

The people see that they have been deluded. They accuse one another of having led them to destruction; but all unite in heaping their bitterest condemnation upon the ministers. Unfaithful pastors have prophesied smooth things; they have led their hearers to make void the law of God and to persecute those who would keep it holy. Now, in their despair, these teachers confess before the world their work of deception. The multitudes are filled with fury. "We are lost!" they cry, "and you are the cause of our ruin;" and they turn upon the false shepherds. The very ones that once admired them most will pronounce the most dreadful curses upon them. The very hands that once crowned them with laurels will be raised for their destruction. The swords which were to slay God's people are now employed to destroy their enemies. Everywhere there is strife and bloodshed.

(9) AFTER THE CLOSE OF PROBATION THE CONTROVERSY BETWEEN GOD AND SATAN EXTENDS TO INCLUDE WHOM?

___

Jeremiah 25:31; 26:21

For six thousand years the great controversy has been in progress; the Son of God and His heavenly messengers have been in conflict with the power of the evil one, to warn, enlighten, and save the children of men. Now all have made their decisions; the wicked have fully united with Satan in his warfare against God. The time has come for God to vindicate the authority of His downtrodden law. Now the controversy is not alone with Satan, but with men. "The Lord hath a controversy with the nations;" "He will give them that are wicked to the sword."

(10) WHAT WILL HAPPEN TO THE WICKED AS THEY SEE CHRIST COMING IN THE CLOUDS?

___

___

___

2 Thessalonians 2:8; Revelation 6:16,17

At the coming of Christ the wicked are blotted from the face of the whole earth—consumed with the spirit of His mouth and destroyed by the brightness of His glory. Christ takes His people to the City of God, and the earth is emptied of its inhabitants. "Behold, the Lord maketh the earth empty, and maketh it waste, and turneth it upside down, and scattereth abroad the inhabitants thereof." "The land shall be utterly emptied, and utterly spoiled: for the Lord hath spoken this word." Isaiah 24:1,3.

(11) WHAT IS THE FUNDAMENTAL CAUSE FOR THE DESTRUCTION OF THE WICKED?

___

___

___

___

___

___

Isaiah 24:5,6

"... Therefore hath the curse devoured the earth, and they that dwell therein are desolate: therefore the inhabitants of the earth are burned." Isaiah 24:5, 6. [Everlasting covenant see Exodus 31:16,17; Ezekiel 20:12; Exodus 20:8,11; Isaiah 66:22,23].

(12) WHAT PHYSICAL EFFECT WILL THE LORD'S COMING HAVE UPON THE EARTH?

___

___

___

___

___

2 Peter 3:10

The whole earth appears like a desolate wilderness. The ruins of cities and villages destroyed by the earthquake, uprooted trees, ragged rocks thrown out by the sea or torn out of the earth itself, are scattered over its surface, while vast caverns mark the spot where the mountains have been rent from their foundations.

(13) WHAT IS THE FATE OF SATAN FOLLOWING THE SECOND COMING OF CHRIST?

___

___

___

___

Revelation 20:2

Now the event takes place foreshadowed in the last solemn service of the Day of Atonement. When the ministration in the holy of holies had been completed, and the sins of Israel had been removed from the sanctuary by virtue of the blood of the sin offering, then the scapegoat was presented alive before the Lord; and in the presence of the congregation the high priest confessed over him "all the iniquities of the children of Israel, and all their transgressions in all their sins, putting them upon the head of the goat." Leviticus 16:21. In like manner, when the work of atonement in the heavenly sanctuary has been completed, then in the presence of God and heavenly angels and the hosts of the redeemed the sins of God's people will be placed upon Satan; he will be declared guilty of all the evil which he has caused them to commit. And as the scapegoat was sent away into a land not inhabited, so Satan will be banished to the desolate earth, an uninhabited and dreary wilderness.

(14) WHAT RESTRICTION DOES GOD PLACE UPON SATAN'S ACTIVITIES DURING THE 1,000 YEARS OF HIS BONDAGE?

____

____

____

Revelation 20:3

Here is to be the home of Satan with his evil angels for a thousand years. Limited to the earth, he will not have access to other worlds to tempt and annoy those who have never fallen. It is in this sense that he is bound: there are none remaining, upon whom he can exercise his power. He is wholly cut off from the work of deception and ruin which for so many centuries has been his sole delight.

For six thousand years, Satan's work of rebellion has "made the earth to tremble." He had "made the world as a wilderness, and destroyed the cities thereof." And he "opened not the house of his prisoners." For six thousand years his prison house has received God's people, and he would have held them captive forever; but Christ had broken his bonds and set the prisoners free. Even the wicked are now placed beyond the power of Satan, and alone with his evil angels he remains to realize the effect of the curse which sin has brought. "The kings of the nations, even all of them, lie in glory, everyone in his own house [the grave]. But thou art cast out thy grave like an abominable branch. . . . Thou shalt not be joined with them in burial, because thou hast destroyed thy land, and slain thy people." Isaiah 14:18-20.

For a thousand years, Satan will wander to and fro in the desolate earth to behold the results of his rebellion against the law of God. During this time his sufferings are intense. Since his fall his life of unceasing activity has banished reflection; but he is now deprived of his power and left to contemplate the part which he has acted since first he rebelled against the government of heaven, and to look forward with trembling and terror to the dreadful future when he must suffer for all the evil that he has done and be punished for the sins that he has caused to be committed.

(15) WHAT WILL BE THE ACTIVITY OF THE REDEEMED DURING THE 1,000 YEARS?

____

____

____

Revelation 20:4

During the thousand years between the first and the second resurrection the judgment of the wicked takes place. The apostle Paul points to this judgment as an event that follows the second advent. "Judge nothing before the time, until the Lord come, who both will bring to light the hidden things of darkness, and will make manifest the counsels of the hearts." 1 Corinthians 4:5. Daniel declares that when the Ancient of Days came, "judgment was given to the saints of the Most High." Daniel 7:22. At this time the righteous reign as kings and priests unto God. . . It is at this time that, as foretold by Paul, "the saints shall judge the world." 1 Corinthians 6:2. In union with Christ they judge the wicked, comparing their acts with the statute book, the Bible, and deciding every case according to the deeds done in the body. Then the portion which the wicked must suffer is meted out, according to their works; and it is recorded against their names in the book of death.

(16) WHO WILL BE INCLUDED IN THIS JUDGMENT?

____

____

1 Corinthians 6:2,3

Satan also and evil angels are judged by Christ and His people. Says Paul: "Know ye not that we shall judge angels?" Verse 3. And Jude declares that "the angels which kept not their first estate, but left their own habitation, He hath reserved in everlasting chains under darkness unto the judgment of the great day." Jude 6.

(17) WHAT WILL TAKE PLACE AT THE CLOSE OF THE 1,000 YEAR PERIOD?

____

____

Revelation 20:5

At the close of the thousand years the second resurrection will take place. Then the wicked will be raised from the dead and appear before God for the execution of "the judgment written." Thus the revelator, after describing the resurrection of the righteous, says: "The rest of the dead lived not again until the thousand years were finished." Revelation 20:5. And Isaiah declares, concerning the wicked: "They shall be gathered together, as prisoners are gathered in the pit, and shall be shut up in the prison, and after many days shall they be visited." Isaiah 24:22.

The Scriptures have revealed to me the momentous events that will end this great controversy. I understand that before the close of this conflict, every individual will have made a decision as to where his loyalty will be placed.

Circle: Yes Undecided

I realize that in his quest for my destruction Satan will employ every method within his power to deceive me and when these fail, persecution may follow.

Circle: Yes Undecided

I am thankful that God in His love and mercy is calling His people out of the false doctrines of Babylon and revealing the truths that will prevent deception. I pray for guidance from the Holy Spirit to discern truth from error so that I will not be among the deceived.

Circle: Yes Undecided

I realize that after all mankind has chosen allegiance God's judgements will bring desolation to this earth. I choose to remain loyal to Him regardless of the cost and am thankful for His promises for my deliverance.

Circle: Yes Undecided

The Controversy Ended - 13

At the close of the thousand years, Christ again returns to the earth. He is accompanied by the host of the redeemed and attended by a retinue of angels. As He descends in terrific majesty He bids the wicked dead arise to receive their doom. They come forth, a mighty host, numberless as the sands of the sea. What a contrast to those who were raised at the first resurrection! The righteous were clothed with immortal youth and beauty. The wicked bear the traces of disease and death.

(1) WHAT WORDS WILL SPRING FORTH FROM UNWILLING LIPS DRIVEN BY THE POWER OF TRUTH?

____

____

____

____

Luke 13:35

Every eye in that vast multitude is turned to behold the glory of the Son of God. With one voice the wicked hosts exclaim: "Blessed is He that cometh in the name of the Lord!" It is not love to Jesus that inspires this utterance. The force of truth urges the words from unwilling lips. As the wicked went into their graves, so they come forth with the same enmity to Christ and the same spirit of rebellion. They are to have no new probation in which to remedy the defects of their past lives. Nothing would be gained by this. A lifetime of transgression has not softened their hearts. A second probation, were it given them, would be occupied as was the first in evading the requirements of God and exciting rebellion against Him.

(2) WHAT DESCENDS FROM HEAVEN AS A "BRIDE PREPARED FOR HER HUSBAND"?

____

____

Revelation 21:2

Christ descends upon the Mount of Olives, whence, after His resurrection, He ascended, and where angels repeated the promise of His return. Says the prophet: "The Lord my God shall come, and all the saints with Thee." "And His feet shall stand in that day upon the Mount of Olives, which is before Jerusalem on the east, and the Mount of Olives shall cleave in the midst thereof, . . . and there shall be a very great valley." "And the Lord shall be king over all the earth: in that day shall there be one Lord, and His name one." Zechariah 14:5, 4, 9. As the New Jerusalem, in its dazzling splendor, comes down out of heaven, it rests upon the place purified and made ready to receive it, and Christ, with His people and the angels, enters the Holy City.

(3) WHAT ACTIVITY WILL SATAN RESUME WHEN THE 1,000 YEARS END AND THE WICKED ARE RESURRECTED?

____

____

____

Revelation 20:7,8

Now Satan prepares for a last mighty struggle for the supremacy. While deprived of his power and cut off from his work of deception, the prince of evil was miserable and dejected; but as the wicked dead are raised and he sees the vast multitudes upon his side, his hopes revive, and he determines not to yield the great controversy. He will marshal all the armies of the lost under his banner and through them endeavor to execute his plans. The wicked are Satan's captives. In rejecting Christ they have accepted the rule of the rebel leader. They are ready to receive his suggestions and to do his bidding. Yet, true to his early cunning, he does not acknowledge himself to be Satan. He claims to be the prince who is the rightful owner of the world and whose inheritance has been unlawfully wrested from him. He represents himself to his deluded subjects as a redeemer, assuring them that his power has brought them forth from their graves and that he is about to rescue them from the most cruel tyranny. The presence of Christ having been removed, Satan works wonders to support his claims. He makes the weak strong and inspires all with his own spirit and energy. He proposes to lead them against the camp of the saints and to take possession of the City of God. With fiendish exultation he points to the unnumbered millions who have been raised from the dead and declares that as their leader he is well able to overthrow the city and regain his throne and his kingdom.

(4) WITH WHAT DOES SCRIPTURE COMPARE THE GREAT THRONG OF THE LOST?

____

____

Revelation 20:8

In that vast throng are multitudes of the long-lived race that existed before the

Flood; men of lofty stature and giant intellect, who, yielding to the control of fallen angels, devoted all their skill and knowledge to the exaltation of themselves; men whose wonderful works of art led the world to idolize their genius, but whose cruelty and evil inventions, defiling the earth and defacing the image of God, caused Him to blot them from the face of His creation. There are kings and generals who conquered nations, valiant men who never lost a battle, proud, ambitious warriors whose approach made kingdoms tremble. In death these experienced no change. As they come up from the grave, they resume the current of their thoughts just where it ceased. They are actuated by the same desire to conquer that ruled them when they fell.

Satan consults with his angels, and then with these kings and conquerors and mighty men. They look upon the strength and numbers on their side, and declare that the army within the city is small in comparison with theirs, and that it can be overcome. They lay their plans to take possession of the riches and glory of the New Jerusalem. All immediately begin to prepare for battle. Skillful artisans construct implements of war. Military leaders, famed for their success, marshal the throngs of warlike men into companies and divisions.

(5) WHAT DOES THIS VAST ARMY ATTEMPT UNDER SATAN'S COMMAND?

____

____

____

Revelation 20:9

At last the order to advance is given, and the countless host moves on—an army such as was never summoned by earthly conquerors, such as the combined forces of all ages since war began on earth could never equal. Satan, the mightiest of warriors, leads the van, and his angels unite their forces for this final struggle. Kings and warriors are in his train, and the multitudes follow in vast companies, each under its appointed leader. With military precision the serried ranks advance over the earth's broken and uneven surface to the City of God. By command of Jesus, the gates of the New Jerusalem are closed, and the armies of Satan surround the city and make ready for the onset.

Now Christ again appears to the view of His enemies. Far above the city, upon a foundation of burnished gold, is a throne, high and lifted up. Upon this throne sits the Son of God, and around Him are the subjects of His kingdom. The power and majesty of Christ no language can describe, no pen portray. The glory of the Eternal Father is enshrouding His Son. The brightness of His presence fills the City of God, and flows out beyond the gates, flooding the whole earth with its radiance.

(6) WHO NUMBERS THE VAST THRONG STANDING BEFORE THE THRONE OF GOD?

____

____

____

Revelation 7:14

Nearest the throne are those who were once zealous in the cause of Satan, but who, plucked as brands from the burning, have followed their Saviour with deep, intense devotion. Next are those who perfected Christian characters in the midst of falsehood and infidelity, those who honored the law of God when the Christian world declared it void, and the millions, of all ages, who were martyred for their faith. And beyond is the "great multitude, which no man could number, of all nations, and kindreds, and people, and tongues, . . .before the throne, and before the Lamb, clothed with white robes, and palms in their hands." Revelation 7:9. Their warfare is ended, their victory won. They have run the race and reached the prize. The palm branch in their hands is a symbol of their triumph, the white robe an emblem of the spotless righteousness of Christ which now is theirs.

(7) WHAT PHRASE OF ADORATION WILL RESOUND FROM THE LIPS OF THE REDEEMED?

____

____

____

Revelation 7:10

The redeemed raise a song of praise that echoes and re-echoes through the vaults of heaven . . . And angel and seraph unite their voices in adoration. As the redeemed have beheld the power and malignity of Satan, they have seen, as never before, that no power but that of Christ could have made them conquerors. In all that shining throng there are none to ascribe salvation to themselves, as if they had prevailed by their own power and goodness. Nothing is said of what they have done or suffered; but the burden of every song, the keynote of every anthem, is: Salvation to our God and unto the Lamb.

(8) FOR WHAT GREAT EVENT ARE THE WICKED DEAD RESURRECTED?

____

____

____

____

Revelation 20:12,13; Romans 14:10,11

In the presence of the assembled inhabitants of earth and heaven the final coronation of the Son of God takes place. And now, invested with supreme majesty and power, the King of kings pronounces sentence upon the rebels against His government and executes justice upon those who have transgressed His law and oppressed His people. Says the prophet of God: "I saw a great white throne, and Him that sat on it, from whose face the earth and the heaven fled away; and there was found no place for them. And I saw the dead, small and great, stand before God; and the books were opened: and another book was opened, which is the book of life: and the dead were judged out of those things which were written in the books, according to their works."

(9) WHAT WILL BE REVEALED AT THE GREAT JUDGMENT?

____

____

____

2 Corinthians 5:10

As soon as the books of record are opened, and the eye of Jesus looks upon the wicked, they are conscious of every sin which they have ever committed. They see just where their feet diverged from the path of purity and holiness, just how far pride and rebellion have carried them in the violation of the law of God. The seductive temptations which they encouraged by indulgence in sin, the blessings perverted, the messengers of God despised, the warnings rejected, the waves of mercy beaten back by the stubborn, unrepentant heart—all appear as if written in letters of fire.

(10) WHAT FACTS DESCRIBED IN THESE VERSES WILL STRIKE

TERROR INTO THE HEARTS OF THE LOST ON JUDGEMENT DAY?

____

____

____

____

____

____

Isaiah 53:3,5; Isaiah 53:1-12

Above the throne is revealed the cross; and like a panoramic view appear the scenes of Adam's temptation and fall, and the successive steps in the great plan of redemption. The Saviour's lowly birth; His early life of simplicity and obedience; His baptism in Jordan; the fast and temptation in the wilderness; His public ministry, unfolding to men heaven's most precious blessings; the days crowded with deeds of love and mercy, the nights of prayer and watching in the solitude of the mountains; the plottings of envy, hate, and malice which repaid His benefits; the awful, mysterious agony in Gethsemane beneath the crushing weight of the sins of the whole world; His betrayal into the hands of the murderous mob; the fearful events of that night of horror—the unresisting prisoner, forsaken by His best-loved disciples, rudely hurried through the streets of Jerusalem; the Son of God exultingly displayed before Annas, arraigned in the high priest's palace, in the judgment hall of Pilate, before the cowardly and cruel Herod, mocked, insulted, tortured, and condemned to die—all are vividly portrayed.

And now before the swaying multitude are revealed the final scenes—the patient Sufferer treading the path to Calvary; the Prince of heaven hanging upon the cross; the haughty priests and the jeering rabble deriding His expiring agony; the supernatural darkness; the heaving earth, the rent rocks, the open graves, marking the moment when the world's Redeemer yielded up His life.

The awful spectacle appears just as it was. Satan, his angels, and his subjects have no power to turn from the picture of their own work. Each actor recalls the part which he performed. Herod, who slew the innocent children of Bethlehem that he might destroy the King of Israel; the base Herodias, upon whose guilty soul rests the blood of John the Baptist; the weak, timeserving Pilate; the mocking soldiers; the priests and rulers and the maddened throng who cried, "His blood be on us, and on our children!"—all behold the enormity of their guilt. They vainly seek to hide from the divine majesty of His countenance, outshining the glory of the sun, while the redeemed cast their crowns at the Saviour's feet, exclaiming: "He died for me!"

(11) WHAT IS THE FINAL FATE OF THE WICKED?

____

____

____

Revelation 20:15; Galations 6:8

The whole wicked world stand arraigned at the bar of God on the charge of high treason against the government of heaven. They have none to plead their cause; they are without excuse; and the sentence of eternal death is pronounced against them.

It is now evident to all that the wages of sin is not noble independence and eternal life, but slavery, ruin, and death. The wicked see what they have forfeited by their life of rebellion. The far more exceeding and eternal weight of glory was despised when offered them; but how desirable it now appears. "All this," cries the lost soul, "I might have had; but I chose to put these things far from me. Oh, strange infatuation! I have exchanged peace, happiness, and honor for wretchedness, infamy, and despair." All see that their exclusion from heaven is just. By their lives they have declared: "We will not have this Man [Jesus] to reign over us."

(12) WHAT SONG OF PRAISE WILL THE REDEEMED PROCLAIM?

____

____

____

____

____

Revelation 15:3

As if entranced, the wicked have looked upon the coronation of the Son of God. They see in His hands the tables of the divine law, the statutes which they have despised and transgressed. They witness the outburst of wonder, rapture, and adoration from the saved; and as the wave of melody sweeps over the multitudes without the city, all with one voice exclaim, "Great and marvelous are Thy works, Lord God Almighty; just and true are Thy ways, Thou King of saints"; and, falling prostrate, they worship the Prince of life.

(13) WHAT TRAIT OF SATAN'S CHARACTER WILL FINALLY BE REVEALED TO THE UNIVERSE?

____

____

____

Ezekiel 28:15-17; Ecclesiastes 12:14

The aim of the great rebel has ever been to justify himself and to prove the divine government responsible for the rebellion. To this end he has bent all the power of his giant intellect. He has worked deliberately and systematically, and with marvelous success, leading vast multitudes to accept his version of the great controversy which has been so long in progress. For thousands of years this chief of conspiracy has palmed off falsehood for truth. But the time has now come when the rebellion is to be finally defeated and the history and character of Satan disclosed. In his last great effort to dethrone Christ, destroy His people, and take possession of the City of God, the archdeceiver has been fully unmasked. Those who have united with him see the total failure of his cause. Christ's followers and the loyal angels behold the full extent of his machinations against the government of God. He is the object of universal abhorrence.

(14) WHAT WILL BE THE RESPONSE OF EVERY CREATED BEING?

____

____

____

____

Philippians 2:10,11

Satan sees that his voluntary rebellion has unfitted him for heaven. He has trained his powers to war against God; the purity, peace, and harmony of heaven would be to him supreme torture. His accusations against the mercy and justice of God are now silenced. The reproach which he has endeavored to cast upon Jehovah rests wholly upon himself. And now Satan bows down and confesses the justice of his sentence.

(15) WHAT TRUTH ABOUT GOD'S GOVERNMENT AND CHARACTER WILL BECOME APPARENT TO THE ENTIRE UNIVERSE?

____

____

____

Psalm 97:2; Psalm 98:9

____

____

____

Revelation 15:4

Every question of truth and error in the long-standing controversy has now been made plain. The results of rebellion, the fruits of setting aside the divine statutes, have been laid open to the view of all created intelligences. The working out of Satan's rule in contrast with the government of God has been presented to the whole universe. Satan's own works have condemned him. God's wisdom, His justice, and His goodness stand fully vindicated. It is seen that all His dealings in the great controversy have been conducted with respect to the eternal good of His people and the good of all the worlds that He has created. "All Thy works shall praise Thee, O Lord; and Thy saints shall bless Thee." Psalm 145:10. The history of sin will stand to all eternity as a witness that with the existence of God's law is bound up the happiness of all the beings He has created. With all the facts of the great controversy in view, the whole universe, both loyal and rebellious, with one accord declare: "Just and true are Thy ways, Thou King of saints."

(16) WHAT IS THE REACTION OF THOSE DECEIVED BY SATAN WHEN HIS CHARACTER AND TRUE MOTIVES HAVE BEEN REVEALED?

____

____

____

Ezekiel 28:19; Ezekiel 28:6-8

Notwithstanding that Satan has been constrained to acknowledge God's justice and to bow to the supremacy of Christ, his character remains unchanged. The spirit of rebellion, like a mighty torrent, again bursts forth. Filled with frenzy, he determines not to yield the great controversy. The time has come for a last desperate struggle against the King of heaven. He rushes into the midst of his subjects and endeavors to inspire them with his own fury and arouse them to instant battle. But of all the countless millions whom he has allured into rebellion, there are none now to acknowledge his supremacy. His power is at an end. The wicked are filled with the same hatred of God that inspires Satan; but they see that their case is hopeless, that they cannot prevail against Jehovah. Their rage is kindled against Satan and those who have been his agents in deception, and with the fury of demons they turn upon them.

(17) WHAT JUST SENTENCE IS GIVEN BY GOD REVEALING THE ULTIMATE FATE OF SATAN?

____

____

____

____

____

____

____

____

Ezekiel 28:16-19

(18) WHAT JUDGMENT IS PRONOUNCED UPON THOSE WHOSE NAMES ARE NOT WRITTEN IN THE BOOK OF LIFE?

Revelation 20:15

"Every battle of the warrior is with confused noise, and garments rolled in blood; but this shall be with burning and fuel of fire." "The indignation of the Lord is upon all nations, and His fury upon all their armies: He hath utterly destroyed them, He hath delivered them to the slaughter." "Upon the wicked He shall rain quick burning coals, fire and brimstone and an horrible tempest: this shall be the portion of their cup." Isaiah 9:5; 34:2; Psalm 11:6, margin. Fire comes down from God out of heaven. The earth is broken up. The weapons concealed in its depths are drawn forth. Devouring flames burst from every yawning chasm. The very rocks are on fire. The day has come that shall burn as an oven. The elements melt with fervent heat, the earth also, and the works that are therein are burned up. Malachi 4:1; 2 Peter 3:10. The earth's surface seems one molten mass—a vast, seething lake of fire. It is the time of the judgment and perdition of ungodly men—"the day of the Lord's vengeance, and the year of recompenses for the controversy of Zion." Isaiah 34:8.

(19) WHAT WILL BE THE BASIS OF GOD'S JUDGEMENT AND THE ULTIMATE DELIVERY OF JUSTICE?

Romans 2:6; Romans 2:7-11; Revelation 20:13; Isaiah 3:10,11

The wicked receive their recompense in the earth. Proverbs 11:31. They "shall be stubble: and the day that cometh shall burn them up, saith the Lord of hosts." Malachi 4:1. Some are destroyed as in a moment, while others suffer many days. All are punished "according to their deeds." The sins of the righteous having been transferred to Satan, he is made to suffer not only for his own rebellion, but for all the sins which he has caused God's people to commit. His punishment is to be far greater than that of those whom he has deceived. After all have perished who fell by his deceptions, he is still to live and suffer on.

(20) WHAT WILL REMAIN OF SATAN AND ALL EVIL AFTER THE CLEANSING FLAMES HAVE STOPPED?

Ezekiel 28:18; Malachi 4:1,3

In the cleansing flames the wicked are at last destroyed, root and branch—Satan the root, his followers the branches. The full penalty of the law has been visited; the demands of justice have been met; and heaven and earth, beholding, declare the righteousness of Jehovah.

(21) HOW DOES SCRIPTURE DESCRIBE THE FINAL FATE OF THE WICKED?

Psalms 104:35; 37:20; Obadiah 16

(22) WHAT PROMISE WILL ALL WHO HAVE EXPERIENCED THE DEVASTATION OF SIN GLADLY CLAIM?

____

____

____

Nahum 1:9

Satan's work of ruin is forever ended. For six thousand years he has wrought his will, filling the earth with woe and causing grief throughout the universe. The whole creation has groaned and travailed together in pain. Now God's creatures are forever delivered from his presence and temptations. "The whole earth is at rest, and is quiet: they [the righteous] break forth into singing." Isaiah 14:7. And a shout of praise and triumph ascends from the whole loyal universe. "The voice of a great multitude," "as the voice of many waters, and as the voice of mighty thunderings," is heard, saying: "Alleluia: for the Lord God omnipotent reigneth." Revelation 19:6.

(23) WHAT PASSES AWAY AND IS REPLACED BY THE NEW?

____

____

____

Revelation 21:1

The fire that consumes the wicked purifies the earth. Every trace of the curse is swept away. No eternally burning hell will keep before the ransomed the fearful consequences of sin.

(24) WHAT SINGLE REMINDER OF SIN WILL CHRIST FOREVER BEAR?

____

____

____

John 20:25

One reminder alone remains: Our Redeemer will ever bear the marks of His crucifixion. Upon His wounded head, upon His side, His hands and feet, are the only traces of the cruel work that sin has wrought. Says the prophet, beholding Christ in His glory: "He had bright beams coming out of His side: and there was the hiding of His power." Habakkuk 3:4, margin. That pierced side whence flowed the crimson stream that reconciled man to God—there is the Saviour's glory, there "the hiding of His power." "Mighty to save," through the sacrifice of redemption, He was therefore strong to execute justice upon them that despised God's mercy. And the tokens of His humiliation are His highest honor; through the eternal ages the wounds of Calvary will show forth His praise and declare His power.

(25) WHAT IS CHRIST PREPARING FOR THE FAITHFUL?

____

____

____

John 14:2; 2 Peter 3:13

A fear of making the future inheritance seem too material has led many to spiritualize away the very truths which lead us to look upon it as our home. Christ assured His disciples that He went to prepare mansions for them in the Father's house. Those who accept the teachings of God's word will not be wholly ignorant concerning the heavenly abode. And yet, "eye hath not seen, nor ear heard, neither have entered into the heart of man, the things which God hath prepared for them that love Him." 1 Corinthians 2:9. Human language is inadequate to describe the reward of the righteous. It will be known only to those who behold it. No finite mind can comprehend the glory of the Paradise of God.

(26) TO WHAT IS THE LAND OF INHERITANCE COMPARED?

____

____

Hebrews 11:14; 11:11-16

____

____

Revelation 3:12

In the Bible the inheritance of the saved is called "a country." . . . There the heavenly Shepherd leads His flock to fountains of living waters. The tree of life yields its fruit every month, and the leaves of the tree are for the service of the nations. There are ever-flowing streams, clear as crystal, and beside them waving trees cast their shadows upon the paths prepared for the ransomed of the Lord. There the widespreading plains swell into hills of beauty, and the mountains of God rear their lofty summits. On those peaceful plains, beside those living streams, God's people, so long pilgrims and wanderers, shall find a home.

(27) WHAT WILL BE THE APPEARANCE OF THE NEW JERUSALEM?

____

____

____

____

Revelation 21:11; 21:10-27

(28) WHAT WILL BE THE ATMOSPHERE IN THE LAND WE INHABIT?

____

____

____

____

Isaiah 32:18; Isaiah 60:18

There, "the wilderness and the solitary place shall be glad for them; and the desert shall rejoice, and blossom as the rose." "Instead of the thorn shall come up the fir tree, and instead of the brier shall come up the myrtle tree." "The wolf also shall dwell with the lamb, and the leopard shall lie down with the kid; . . . and a little child shall lead them." "They shall not hurt nor destroy in all My holy mountain," saith the Lord. Isaiah 35:1; 55:13; 11:6, 9.

(29) WHAT WONDERFUL ACTIVITIES WILL THE REDEEMED HAVE THE JOY OF PERFORMING IN THE NEW EARTH?

____

____

Isaiah 65:21,22

(30) WHAT 4 EVIDENCES OF SIN WILL NO LONGER EXIST?

____

____

____

Revelation 21:4; Isaiah 33:24

Pain cannot exist in the atmosphere of heaven. There will be no more tears, no funeral trains, no badges of mourning. . . . for the former things are passed away." "The inhabitant shall not say, I am sick: the people that dwell therein shall be forgiven their iniquity."

(31) WHAT WILL BE THE SOURCE OF LIGHT IN THE CITY OF GOD?

____

____

Revelation 22:5

In the City of God "there shall be no night." None will need or desire repose. There will be no weariness in doing the will of God and offering praise to His name. We shall ever feel the freshness of the morning and shall ever be far from its close. . . .The light of the sun will be superseded by a radiance which is not painfully dazzling, yet which immeasurably surpasses the brightness of our noontide. The glory of God and the Lamb floods the Holy City with unfading light. The redeemed walk in the sunless glory of perpetual day.

(32) WHOSE DIVINE PRESENCE WILL NO LONGER BEAR THE VEIL OF AN EARTHLY TEMPLE?

____

____

Revelation 21:22

The people of God are privileged to hold open communion with the Father and the Son. "Now we see through a glass, darkly." 1 Corinthians 13:12. We behold the image of God reflected, as in a mirror, in the works of nature and in His dealings with men; but then we shall see Him face to face, without a dimming veil between. We shall stand in His presence and behold the glory of His countenance.

There the redeemed shall know, even as also they are known. The loves and sympathies which God Himself has planted in the soul shall there find truest and sweetest exercise. The pure communion with holy beings, the harmonious social life with the blessed angels and with the faithful ones of all ages who have washed their robes and made them white in the blood of the Lamb, the sacred ties that bind together "the whole family in heaven and earth" (Eph. 3:15)—these help to constitute the happiness of the redeemed.

There, immortal minds will contemplate with never-failing delight the wonders of creative power, the mysteries of redeeming love. There will be no cruel, deceiving foe to tempt to forgetfulness of God. Every faculty will be developed, every capacity increased. The acquirement of knowledge will not weary the mind or exhaust the energies. There the grandest enterprises may be carried forward, the loftiest aspirations reached, the highest ambitions realized; and still there will arise new heights to surmount, new wonders to admire, new truths to comprehend, fresh objects to call forth the powers of mind and soul and body.

(33) WHAT TESTIMONY WILL RESOUND FROM THE REDEEMED THROUGHOUT ETERNITY?

____

____

____

____

Revelation 5:12

All the treasures of the universe will be open to the study of God's redeemed. Unfettered by mortality, they wing their tireless flight to worlds afar—worlds that thrilled with sorrow at the spectacle of human woe and rang with songs of gladness at the tidings of a ransomed soul. With unutterable delight the children of earth enter into the joy and the wisdom of unfallen beings. They share the treasures of knowledge and understanding gained through ages upon ages in contemplation of God's handiwork. With undimmed vision they gaze upon the glory of creation—suns and stars and systems, all in their appointed order circling the throne of Deity. Upon all things, from the least to the greatest, the Creator's name is written, and in all are the riches of His power displayed.

(34) WHAT SONG WILL FLOW FROM THE LIPS OF ALL GOD'S

REDEEMED AS THEY REFLECT UPON THE OUTCOME OF THE GREAT CONTROVERSY?

____

____

____

____

Revelation 5:13

And the years of eternity, as they roll, will bring richer and still more glorious revelations of God and of Christ. As knowledge is progressive, so will love, reverence, and happiness increase. The more men learn of God, the greater will be their admiration of His character. As Jesus opens before them the riches of redemption and the amazing achievements in the great controversy with Satan, the hearts of the ransomed thrill with more fervent devotion, and with more rapturous joy they sweep the harps of gold; and ten thousand times ten thousand and thousands of thousands of voices unite to swell the mighty chorus of praise.

The great controversy is ended. Sin and sinners are no more. The entire universe is clean. One pulse of harmony and gladness beats through the vast creation. From Him who created all, flow life and light and gladness, throughout the realms of illimitable space. From the minutest atom to the greatest world, all things, animate and inanimate, in their unshadowed beauty and perfect joy, declare that God is love.

I am thankful that, in love, God has revealed through Scripture the life-giving knowledge of the Great Controversy. I realize the final battleground of this struggle is my heart and the ultimate issue of the controversy is my allegiance.

Circle: Yes Undecided

I now understand how the controversy began, the principles involved, how long it will continue, and how it will end. I am thankful that I am now aware of Satan's deceptions and better prepared to make the critical decisions that will determine my eternal destiny.

Circle: Yes Undecided

I am looking forward to the years of eternity that will bring a richer and still more glorious revelation in the knowledge of God and Christ.

Circle: Yes Undecided

My sincere prayer is, "Dear Lord, I give my life as a humble offering. Change me by Your grace into Your image. Please give me confidence to share these lifegiving messages with others. Provide me the wisdom and grace to live in obedience to Your holy laws. Give me the strength to remain faithful to this important conviction at any cost. Please come soon Lord Jesus!

Circle: Yes Undecided

The wording of your answers will vary according to the translation of the Bible you use, but the meaning should remain constant.

Lesson 1

(1) God cannot be tempted with evil and He tempts no man.
(2) Sin is to break or transgress the law.
(3) Justice, judgement, mercy, and truth.
(4) Lucifer or Son of the Morning, later called Satan or a Serpent.
(5) He was created perfect by God, blameless in all ways.
(6) His heart was filled with pride because of his beauty and brightness.
(7) The wages of sin is death.
(8) To have a throne above God's and be like the Most High.
(9) As a murderer and the father of lies.
(10) Kindness, tolerance, and patience.
(11) A third.
(12) Perverted ways will be known.
(13) Because in His justice and great righteousness He does not oppress.
(14) To a conflict that resulted in the eviction of Satan and his followers from heaven.
(15) The earth.
(16) He is merciful, gracious, long-suffering, forgiving and full of truth and goodness.
(17) He gave His only Son for our redemption.
(18) "Crucify Him".
(19) Reconciled the world to Himself.
(20) To fulfill the law–not destroy it.
(21) Every knee will bow and tongue confess the Lordship of Christ.
(22) "It is finished."
(23) They will be destroyed, they shall be stubble without root or branch.
(24) Sin will be destroyed, affliction will not rise up a second time.

Lesson 2

(1) He (God) will put enmity (hatred) between Thee (Satan) and the Woman (the true church).
(2) You must not eat from the Tree of Knowledge of Good and Evil. If you eat you will surely die.
(3) Eve defied God and took and ate of the fruit.
(4) The testing of your faith.
(5) The devil.
(6) Because man was created in the image of God.
(7) We may become partakers of the divine nature.
(8) He was without sin.
(9) Everyone who lives Godly lives will be persecuted.
(10) Submit to God and resist the devil.
(11) To blind the minds of God's believers.
(12) Do not set foot on the path of the wicked or walk in the ways of evil men.
(13) Do not envy the wicked or desire their company.
(14) God is our refuge and strength.
(15) He is like a roaring lion seeking whom he may devour.
(16) The armor of God.
(17) The Word of God.
(18) God will not allow us to be tempted above what we are able to bear and He will provide a way of escape from every temptation.

Lesson 3

(1) The rulers, powers, and authorities of darkness.
(2) Around God's throne.
(3) Demons or Devils.
(4) The earth.
(5) A little lower then the angels.
(6) Thousands and thousands and ten thousand times ten thousand.
(7) One third.
(8) Like burning coals of fire or like torches. Also like flashes of lightning.
(9) A single angel slew a hundred and eighty five thousand men in one night.
(10) Ministering spirits sent to serve those who will inherit salvation.
(11) Protect and deliver those who fear (respect) the Lord.
(12) They chose to sin.
(13) Miraculous signs.
(14) Many People.
(15) A legion.
(16) The Lord Jesus Christ.
(17) A sorcerer.
(18) He is beautiful and full of splendor or brightness.
(19) (a) Put on the full armor of God.
(b) Study to show ourselves approved.

(20) He guards His faithful ones and delivers them from the hand of evil.

Lesson 4

(1) To deceive the nations.
(2) Submit ourselves to God and resist the devil.
(3) Walk in the Spirit and you will not fulfill the lusts of the flesh.
(4) The worries of life, love of riches, and other earthly desires entering in and crowding out the Word.
(5) He uses them to cause divisions, plant seeds of doubt concerning doctrine.
(6) By their fruits.
(7) The truth sets us free!
(8) They will wrestle them to their own destruction.
(9) Those who would think to alter God's Word will receive the plagues described therein.
(10) It will make wise the simple.
(11) He sees it as foolishness.
(12) Profane talk and foolish arguments falsely called science.
(13) His judgements are unsearchable and ways past finding out.
(14) Those that have not received the love for the truth that they may be saved.
(15) Making the Word of God to have no effect because of traditions.
(16) Your traditions may lead you to reject the commandments of God.
(17) Those who ask.
(18) It is better to trust the Lord than put our confidence in man.
(19) It leads us to depart from God and have a hardened heart because of the deceitfulness of sin.
(20) To be filled with doubt and lack faith.
(21) What we sow we shall also reap.
(22) Make the choice to do God's will and then continue in the light we have been given.
(23) (a) Through hearing the Word of God.
(b) Cry out for God to help your unbelief.
(24) Those who seek will find.
(25) Trials purify our faith as flames purify gold.
(26) Not by our might or power but by the Spirit of the Lord.
(27) As His followers He has given us power over the enemy.
(28) Watch and pray.

Lesson 5

(1) We are servants to whom we obey.
(2) You will not surely die.
(3) (a) Separation from God.
(b) They were banished from the tree of life and the garden.
(4) Sin is transgression of the law.
(5) The wages of sin is death.
(6) Accepting Jesus Christ who has destroyed death and brought life and immortality to light through the gospel.
(7) It will surely die.
(8) An angel with a flaming sword was sent to guard the tree of life.
(9) Destroyed in the fires of hell.
(10) (a) He takes no pleasure in the death of the wicked.
(b) He doesn't want anyone to perish but all to come to repentance.
(11) (a) Righteousness
(b) Justice
(c) Love
(d) Faithfulness
(12) Only ashes.
(13) Fire will consume him, reduce him to ashes and will be no more.
(14) The wine of her fornication or adulteries.
(15) He will come and give each one their just reward.
(16) (a) We must first thirst.
(b) We must overcome.
(17) (a) Mercy, graciousness, long-suffering, abundant goodness, and forgiveness for rebellion and sin but He will by no means clear those who choose to remain guilty.
(b) All the wicked He will destroy.
(18) Come now let us reason together though your sins are as scarlet they shall be white as snow.
(19) They will call for the rocks and mountains to fall on them to hide them from His face.
(20) He that is unjust, let him be unjust still and he that is righteous, let him be righteous still.
(21) Every tendency and thought of man

became continually evil.

(22) Because by the trespass of one man death reigned how much more will those who accept God's grace gain life through the one man Jesus.

(23) Every person will be rewarded according to his works.

(24) (a) The wages of sin is death.
(b) They shall be as though they had not been.

(25) The dead know nothing, their memory is gone, and their emotions of love, hate, and envy are departed.

(26) The living praise You but those in the grave cannot sing Your praises.

(27) He died, was buried and his tomb remains today.

(28) They will come from their graves.

(29) He is coming with His reward on that day.

(30) I go to prepare a place for you then I will come again and receive you unto Myself.

(31) The great judgement before God's throne.

(32) Asleep in the dust.

(33) Death where is your sting, grave where is your victory!

Lesson 6

(1) The dead do not return.

(2) The ability to perform great signs and miracles.

(3) Samuel the prophet.

(4) (a) Counterfeit miracles
(b) Signs and wonders
(c) Every sort of evil imaginable

(5) He masquerades as an angel of light.

(6) It is of the devil.

(7) God is the Giver, humility is the basis.

(8) Temperance in all things.

(9) Do not turn to mediums or seek out spiritualists because they will defile you.

(10) The death penalty.

(11) The Word of God is truth.

(12) Spiritualism gives false claims that God's divine power is its source.

(13) Study God's Word to show ourselves approved.

(14) Sin separates us from God.

(15) Because they refuse to love the truth.

(16) Fallen angels and the powers of evil.

(17) The dead know not anything.

(18) Since we have followed His commandments He will keep us from "the hour of trial."

(19) Destruction due to lack of knowledge.

(20) You will not surely die.

(21) They will be swept away and destroyed.

Lesson 7

(1) If you break one you are as guilty as if you broke them all.

(2) To make us blind to sin because the law makes us aware of sin.

(3) It is a lamp for our feet and a light for our path.

(4) Rejection of the Word of the Lord.

(5) Rejection of truth leads to the rejection of Christ.

(6) All His righteous laws are eternal.

(7) Lawlessness is sin.

(8) We will reap what we have sown.

(9) Long life and prosperity.

(10) Justice and righteousness are turned away and honesty cannot enter.

(11) Hearts become calloused and unfeeling.

(12) All God's laws are eternal.

(13) They will keep God's commandments

(14) The seventh day of the week.

(15) He would "think" to change set times and laws.

(16) Deceptive philosophy and human traditions.

(17) Having a form of godliness but denial of the power thereof.

(18) The earth dries up and withers, it is defiled by its inhabitants because they have transgressed the laws.

(19) Restrict God's loyal followers from places of worship and kill them and believe they are doing this for God.

(20) Spirits of devils working great signs and miracles to try and deceive even the elect.

(21) The devil, our adversary, goes about as a roaring lion, seeking whom he may devour.

(22) They keep the commandments of God and have the testimony of Jesus.

(23) Restrictions will be imposed prohibiting God's commandment keepers from buying or selling.

Lesson 8

(1) Living by every Word of God.
(2) God Himself will restore you making you strong, firm, and steadfast.
(3) They are given to us and our children that we may follow the words of God's law and to teach us what is coming so we will have encouragement and hope.
(4) (a) Fear (respect) God and give glory for the hour of His judgement has come.
(b) Babylon is fallen, that great city, which made all nations drink of her wine of adulteries or fornications (false doctrines).
(c) If anyone worships the beast or his image and therefore received his mark will receive the judgements of God.
(5) The time will come when they will not endure sound doctrine and will turn away from the truth.
(6) If they do not speak to the law and the testimony of God's Word there is no light in them.
(7) Search the Scriptures daily with an open mind.
(8) They despised and rejected Christ.
(9) Study to show thyself approved of God, a workman that needeth not to be ashamed, rightly dividing the Word of truth.
(10) There will be false teachers who will bring in false doctrine.
(11) We are each responsible to search it out for ourselves.
(12) There is a way that seemeth right unto a man, but the end thereof are the ways of death.
(13) In a topical fashion–precept upon precept; line upon line.
(14) We shall know of the doctrine.
(15) (a) Communion with Him in prayer.
(b) Then seek to find Him and the truth He reveals with all our heart.
(16) Those who continue in His Word will be His disciples and know the truth.
(17) Spiritual matters are spiritually discerned.
(18) The Father will send the Holy Spirit to bring things to our remembrance.
(19) God allows those who choose to turn away from the knowledge of the Bible to reap the fruit of their depraved minds.
(20) They will be refined like silver and gold, they will call on His name and He will answer, He will call us His people and we will call Him our Lord and God.

Lesson 9

(1) Babylon is fallen because she made all nations drink of the maddening wine of her adulteries (false doctrines).
(2) Come out of her My people so you do not take part in her sins and receive not her plagues.
(3) Reached unto heaven.
(4) (a) Economic sanctions preventing them from buying or selling.
(b) The death penalty.
(5) If any man worship the beast and his image and receive his mark he shall experience the fury of God's wrath.
(6) It is a sign between us and God showing He is our Lord.
(7) Not the natural children (literal blood line) but those who claim the promise.
(8) They will choose teachers who say things their ears want to hear.
(9) We should preach the Word at all times correcting, rebuking, and encouraging.
(10) Those that Christ died for and calls His friends He has chosen to go bear fruit for His kingdom.
(11) You will know the truth and the truth will make you free!
(12) Satan, the dragon, will use his human instruments to make war against those who obey God's commandments and hold to the testimony of Jesus.
(13) There will be betrayal between family members to the point of death.
(14) Obedience to God's commands.
(15) Decide to obey God over man.
(16) From God who does not weary and whose understanding has no end for He strengthens the weary and weak.
(17) Because we follow Christ, we will be hated, persecuted, and possibly put to death.
(18) The Lord directs the heart of our

rulers where He pleases.
(19) He will pour out His Spirit on all His people.
(20) Perform great and miraculous signs in an effort to deceive the inhabitants of the earth.
(21) Many will prophesy, have visions and dreams, and everyone who calls on the name of the Lord will be saved.

Lesson 10

(1) "...He which is filthy, let him be filthy still: and he that is righteous, let him be righteous still . . ."
(2) A great "Time of trouble" such as not happened from the beginning.
(3) Four angels encompassing the earth.
(4) Obey God's commandments and remain faithful to Jesus.
(5) They claim to honour Me but their hearts are far from Me. They worship in vain teaching their own doctrines.
(6) They will seek to kill God's true followers thinking it is God's will.
(7) Like Jacob's "Time of trouble."
(8) Satan.
(9) He will become enraged and make war against those who obey God's law.
(10) Their faith.
(11) He will keep them from the hour of temptation, which shall come upon all the world.
(12) God will consider them detestable or an abomination.
(13) If we are faithful in few things He will put us in charge of many.
(14) Sorrow for sin.
(15) When we are tested we will come forth as gold.
(16) The effectual fervent prayer.
(17) The righteous will live by faith.
(18) Be joyful always and pray continually giving thanks in all circumstances.
(19) We are each responsible to work out our own salvation with fear and trembling.
(20) We may partake of His divine nature and escape the corruption of the world.
(21) (a) Counterfeit miracles
(b) Signs
(c) Wonders
(22) False christs and false prophets performing miracles.
(23) By the law and testimony in God's Word.
(24) He will appear in the clouds of the sky with power and great glory.
(25) Because they had no love for the truth.
(26) (a) Lust of the flesh.
(b) Lust of the eyes.
(c) Pride of life.
(27) The mountains.
(28) He will not forget us. We are engraved in the palms of His hands.
(29) His "strange work" or "strange act".
(30) (a) Painful sores.
(b) Sea turned to blood.
(c) Rivers and springs turned to blood.
(d) Scorching heat of the sun.
(e) Terrible darkness.
(f) Waters dried up.
(g) Great earth quake.
(31) Bread and water.
(32) "I will not let Thee go, except Thou bless me."
(33) The angel of the Lord!
(34) He will save us from the fowler's snare, from pestilence, and the plagues. Thousands will fall around us but we will be protected. We will observe the punishment of the wicked.

Lesson 11

(1) Because they have remained faithful He will keep them from the hour of temptation.
(2) "Lo, this is our God; we have waited for Him, and He will save us..."
(3) "It is done!"
(4) Lightning, thunder, and an earthquake as has never occurred before.
(5) Every eye shall see Him.
(6) They will call out for the mountains and rocks to fall on them to hide them from His face who sits on the throne.
(7) God is our refuge and strength, a very present help in trouble Therefore will not we fear.
(8) His righteousness because God is judge Himself.
(9) His Word is true and His righteous laws are eternal.
(10) If we do not warn them we will be held accountable for his blood.
(11) In the clouds of heaven.

(12) His splendor will cover the heavens with the brightness of lightning.
(13) All faces turn to paleness, they grab their loins as if in child birth.
(14) Hereafter shall ye see the Son of man sitting on the right hand of Power, and coming in the clouds of heaven.
(15) Death, where is thy sting? Grave, where is thy victory?
(16) We will be changed, God will give us immortality.
(17) They shall be taken up together in the clouds, to meet the Lord in the air.
(18) A crown of glory that will never fade.
(19) Come you bless of my Father, inherit the kingdom prepared for you from the foundation of the world.
(20) The "144,000" who have been redeemed from the earth.
(21) (a) These are the ones who came through the "Great tribulation."
(b) These are the ones who did not defile themselves with women (fallen churches.)
(22) He will love much who is forgiven much.
(23) To remove the disgrace from His people.
(24) The "mystery of godliness."
(25) To comprehend with all saints what is the breadth, and length, and depth, and height of the love of Christ.

Lesson 12

(1) Come out of her my people so you will not share in her sins, so you will not receive her plagues.
(2) Plagues will overtake her, mourning, and famine. She will be consumed by fire.
(3) They neglected the hungry, the stranger, the naked, the sick, and those in prison–they failed to demonstrate the principle of love and seeking first the kingdom of heaven.
(4) With true repentance (sorrow for sin) the sinner will turn from his ways.
(5) They are saved from the Fowler's snare; from deadly pestilence; they are protected by His wings of refuge; they will not fear bodily harm or the plagues that destroy the wicked; thousands will fall around them but they will not be harmed.
(6) God will bestow punishment on them for the evil they have done.
(7) That all of God's Words are true and His righteous laws are eternal.
(8) Stricken with by panic they will attack one another.
(9) With the nations.
(10) Will be destroyed by the splendor of His coming.
(11) Because they have transgressed the laws, changed the ordinance, broken the everlasting covenant.
(12) The heavens will disappear with a roar, the elements will be destroyed by fire, and the earth will be laid bare.
(13) He is bound to this desolate earth for a thousand years to reflect on his ways.
(14) He will be kept from deceiving the nations.
(15) They will be given authority to judge and reign with Him a thousand years.
(16) The fallen angels.
(17) The resurrection of the wicked that were destroyed at the second coming of Chirst–the second resurrection.

Lesson 13

(1) "Blessed is He that cometh in the name of the Lord."
(2) The Holy City, the New Jerusalem.
(3) The deception of the nations.
(4) The number of whom is as the sand of the sea.
(5) To surround and overtake the city.
(6) These are they who have come out of the great tribulation and have washed their robs in the blood of the Lamb.
(7) They will proclaim, "Salvation to our God which sitteth upon the throne, and unto the Lamb."
(8) The great judgement before the throne of God.
(9) Things done in the body–good and bad.
(10) He was despised and rejected by men. He was pierced for our transgressions and crushed for our iniquities.
(11) Destruction in the lake of fire.
(12) The song of Moses and the song of the Lamb–Great and marvelous are Your deeds, Lord God Almighty. Just and true are your ways.
(13) The pride that resulted in wickedness and violence.

(14) Every knee will bow and every tongue confess that Jesus Christ is Lord to the glory of the Father.
(15) (A) God's government is based on righteousness and justice.
(B) His character is holy and His righteousness will be revealed.
(16) They will be appalled at him.
(17) "I will destroy thee, O covering cherub, from the midst of the stones of fire. . . . I will cast thee to the ground, I will lay thee before kings, that they may behold thee. . . . I will bring thee to ashes upon the earth in the sight of all them that behold thee. . . . Thou shalt be a terror, and never shalt thou be any more."
(18) Whoever is not found in the Book of Life will be cast into the lake of fire.
(19) God will reward each person according to what they have done.
(20) He and his companions will be reduced to ashes.
(21) They will vanish from the earth and be no more.
(22) Affliction shall not rise a second time.
(23) The first earth passes away and is replaced by the earth made new.
(24) Scars on His hands and side.
(25) A new heaven and a new earth to be the home of the righteous.
(26) (a) "A Country."
(b) The "New Jerusalem."
(27) It is described as having the glory of God: and her light was like unto a stone most precious, even like a jasper stone, clear as crystal.
(28) Peaceable habitation, and in sure dwellings, and quiet resting places.
(29) Build houses and plant vineyards.
(30) Death, crying, sorrow, or pain.
(31) The Lord God gives the light.
(32) Lord God Almighty and the Lamb.
(33) Worthy is the Lamb that was slain to receive power, and riches, and wisdom, and strength, and honor, and glory, and blessing.
(34) Blessing, and honor, and glory, and power, be unto Him that sitteth upon the throne, and unto the Lamb for ever and ever.

Appendix A
Obedience –The True Test of Loyalty

God, in His great wisdom, has set up fundamental laws based on mercy, truth, and justice [Ps.97:2]. His love-based laws are not restrictive but rather are a source of security and happiness to those who wisely abide [Ps.119:1]. By definition, sin is separation from God [Isa.59:1-2] and caused by transgression of His love-based laws [1Jn.3:4]. God could foresee that, if left unchecked, sin would spread throughout the universe with the effect of a malignant cancer. To prevent this He declared the penalty of death for violation of the law [Rom.6:23]. God demonstrated to the universe His perfect balance of justice and mercy [Ps.89:14] by providing a way of salvation for the truly repentant transgressors [1Pet.1:20].

The great controversy continues within us and it is all about obedient allegiance of the heart. Satan's strategy is to gain our allegiance by convincing us that the law–the very tool that makes us aware of our sins and calls us to obedience, is of none effect. He knows that without the law in place our course towards sin and the separation it brings is inevitable [Pv.5:22]. Cleverly, Satan has brought about the infiltration of this false doctrine and the cry resounding from the masses is, "God's laws are void!" Colossians 2:14 is quoted that states that the ordinances against us were *"nailed to the cross."* To read but three verses further [Col.2:17] makes the issue perfectly clear–*"these are a shadow of things to come"* [Eph.2:14]. The ten commandment law and the ceremonial laws are distinctly separate [Deut.31:26; Ex.40:20]. At the moment of Christ's death an unseen hand tore the temple veil from top to bottom to mark the end of these ordinances that dictated the sacrificial practices [Matt.27:51; Mk.15:38]. They were at that moment fulfilled by the lamb of God dying for the sins of the world. The laws that ceased were the ceremonial laws and practices of the sacrificial system that pointed to Christ and were a shadow of the cross [2 Chron.8:13,14; Lev.23:37,38] that was yet to come. The current validity of the ten

Commandments is confirmed in the final chapters of Revelation where we are told that God's people, who ultimately enter heaven, will be commandment keepers [Rev.14:12; Rev.22:14 KJV].

The law is simply a mirror to reflect the condition of our heart [Ez.11:19,20]. To do away with the law is to take away the knowledge of sin [Rom.5:13]. God is love [1Jn.4:8] and the ten commandment law is simply a written explanation of how to demonstrate love. The first four commandments show love and respect for God and the last six for our fellow man [Mk.12:29-31].

God has specifically said, *"If ye love me, keep my commandments"* [1Jn.5:3; Jn.14:15,21,23,24]. The keeping of His commandments out of love makes Him our Lord because we are servants to whom we obey [Rom.6:16]. It is a blessing to obey [Deut.11:27,28]. To show respect to God by obedience to His commandments is the whole duty of man [Ecc.12:13]; He is the Author of Salvation to those who obey [Heb.5:9], and He promises to send the Spirit of Truth to those who obey [Jn.14:16]. At the judgement many will say, "Lord, Lord... but then I will profess unto them, I never knew you: depart from me, ye that work iniquity." The definition of iniquity is violation of the law. The highest form of worship is to love Him enough to obey [2Jn.1:6] and to claim to worship and then intentionally not obey is contradictory– seeking a form of Godliness but denying the authority and power thereof [2Tim.3:1-5].

We are now in a dilema. Like Paul, we see the significance of obedience of the law and that we should obey but we give in to the flesh [Rom.7:19]. Our natures are evil [Ecc.9:3], we are all sinners [Rom.3:23], our righteousness is as filthy rags [Isa.64:6]. In our heart we have the conviction to obey but, with pure motives, in ourselves we do not possess the ability [Jer.13:23].

The good news is we can come to Christ just as we are –wretched and miseralbly lost in sin–and claim the blood that was shed at the cross. By the blood of Jesus we are forgiven of our sins and freed from the ***condemnation and penalty*** of the law [Gal.3:13; Rom.5:8-11]. Then, after full surrender, He will replace our sin-hardened hearts with hearts of love [Ezek.11:19]. We find peace and contenment [Matt.11:28-30; Jn.14:27] as He writes the commandments of love in our hearts [Heb.10:16]. We spend time with Him he demonstrates His character in us by giving us the ability to keep His commandments [Ez.11:20]. By faith [Gal.3:6] we are privileged to become partakers in His divine nature and escape the corruption and lust of this world [Pet.1:4]. We are given the power to obey by His Spirit [Acts 5:32]. The curse of condemnation is gone and the blessing of the law remains as a light unto our path [Ps.37:31; Jam.1:23-25].

Appendix B
The History of the Sabbath

At the end of creation week God set aside a special time and "rested" from all His work. God did not "rest" due to physical exhaustion. He rested, blessed, and made holy the Sabbath so that by His command and example we would be blessed with this weekly memorial of Him as our Lord and Creator [Gen.2:1-3]. He stamped His seal of authority on this specific time each week and asked us to set aside our secular activities and spend this time with Him. But Satan's aim is to keep us so preoccupied with the issues of life that we fail to know or experience the true blessing that observing the fourth commandment brings [Isa.56:2; 58:13,14; Deut.5:29; Heb.4:4-9; Lev.26:2-4; Rev. 22:14].

The Bible clearly outlines the institution of the Sabbath from creation to its observance in the earth made new. The Sabbath was a gift to all mankind at creation 2,000 years before Abraham, the first Jew, existed. At the end of creation week God rested from His creative work and instituted the Sabbath for man [Gen.2:3; Mk.2:27]. Sabbath worship was carried on by the Patriarchs until, due to their cruel treatment during the period of slavery in Egypt, they ceased to observe it. After leaving Egypt they were reminded of its importance by God's provision of a double portion of manna on Friday so they could honor His Sabbath [Ex.16:4,5]. This occurred before the law was given at Mount Sinai confirming it existed prior to Sinai. Then, at Sinai, God reinforced the existence, sacredness, and importance of the 4th commandment by saying "Remember" [Ex.20:8].

The practice of Sabbath observance was continued on by those entering the land of Canaan and was proclaimed by the Prophets and kept by God's faithful [Neh.13:15]. Years later Christ came as our example [1Pet.2:21] and faithfully kept the Sabbath [Luk.4:16; Mk.1:21; 6:2]. Even in His crucifixion and death He observed the Sabbath by resting in the tomb until the first day of the week. There is no record of Him asking for the day to be changed. He specifically said He came to fulfill the law [Matt.5:17,18] and made a statement that indicates the Sabbath would still be considered holy, years after His death when Jerusalem would be destroyed [Mat.24:20]. It is evident that no directions were given by Christ for the observance of Sunday because some of his closest followers prepared his body for burial and then observed the Sabbath "according to the commandment" [Luk.23:56 KJV; Mk.16:1] and continued to observe the Sabbath from that point forward [Act.18:4, 13:27, 13:14, 13:42, 15:21, 17:2].

In the New Testament book of Hebrews, written following Christ's death and resurrection, Sabbath observance was reiterated [Heb.4:8-11]. We are told that the Sabbath is a perpetual covenant [Ex.31:16]– a sign of sanctification in our lives from God [Ez.20:12; Ex.31:13]. We are also told that following the close of this world's history when we enter the new earth we will be observing the seventh day Sabbath [Isa.66:22,23].

With no directions given for a change prior to Christ's death, a change from Sabbath to Sunday worship was not a part of the New Covenant. For something to be part of someone's last will and testament it has to be stated before death [Heb.9:16-18; Gal.3:15].

Appendix C
The History of Sunday Observance

Historical records verify that men in both the church and government instituted the tradition that Sunday worship be observed in honor of Christ's resurrection but Scripture has ordained baptism and communion [Rom.6:4; 1 Pet.3:21; Col. 2:12] for this purpose [Luk.22:19]. The word "Sunday" does not occur in the King James Version of Scripture and the phrase "the first day of the week" is mentioned only eight times, each without any command for a change [Matt.28:1; Mk.16:2; 16:9; Luk.24:1; Jn.20:1; 20:19; Acts20:7; 1Cor.16:2]. Traditions, especially if they involve worshipping the Lord, are great, but we are warned that they must not interfere with the law of God [Matt.15:3; Col.2:8; Acts 5:29].

Study of historical sources reveal the transition from Saturday to Sunday observance and also the institution that claims responsibility for the attempted change. The transition from Saturday to Sunday worship was not immediately implemented following Christ's death but was a slow process that occurred over time.

"Sunday, the first day of the week. Its English name and its German name (Sonntag) are drived from the Latin dies solis, "sun's day," the name of a pagan Roman holiday . . . In the early days of Christianity, Sunday began to replace the Sabbath and to be observed to honor the resurrection of Christ. Sunday was instituted as a day of rest, consecrated especially to the service of God, by the Roman emperor Constantine the Great. Since the 4th century, ecclesiastical and civil legislation has frequently regulated work on Sunday and service attendance. In the United States, laws limiting business activity and amusements on Sunday have become known as blue laws." [Microsoft Encarta Encyclopedia].

The institution of the Papal church of Rome proudly claims authority above God in this attempted change of the Lord's holy day. The following are some published statements from the Catholic Church proudly claiming full responsibility:

Question - Have you any other way of proving that the church (Roman Catholic) has power to institute festivals of precept? Answer - "Had she not such power, she could not have done that in which all modern religionists agree with her–she could not have substituted the observance of Saturday, the seventh day, a change for which there is no Scriptural authority." **A Doctrinal Catechism, by S. Keenan, P.174, 354.**

"The observance of Sunday by the Protestants is an homage they pay, in spite of themselves, to the authority of the Catholic Church." **Plain Talk About Protestantism, by Father Segur, P.213.**

"The Catholic church by virtue of her divine mission changed the day from Saturday to Sunday." **The Convert's Catechism of Catholic Doctrine, P.50, 3rd edition.**

"Reason and common sense demand the acceptance of one or the other alternatives; either Protestism and keeping Saturday, or Catholicity and keeping of Sunday. Compromise is impossible." **American Catholic Quarterly Review, Jan.1883.**

"If you look to the Bible as an authority for the observance of the day (Sunday), you will not find it. It is well to remind the Presbyterians, Methodists, Baptists, and all other Christians outside the pale of the Mother Church, that the Bible does not support them anywhere in the observance of Sunday." **Clifton Tracts, Vol.4, P.15.**

This attempted change was predicted in the book of Daniel, *"... he shall speak great words against the most High, and shall wear out the saints of the most High, and think to change times and laws..."* [Dan.7:25]. The only law involving time is the 4th Commandment [Ex.20:3-17].

Appendix D
Does the Day We Observe Matter?

Does it matter the specific day we "remember" or how we observe it? The 4th Commandment is located in the heart of God's law. It is the one Commandment that on a specific day, and in a specific way, serves as a perpetual memorial and honor to God as our Creator and Lord. Is full obedience important? Does it matter? When you tell your toddler to do something, do you expect the child to fully understand and agree before obeying? No, you expect obedience out of love, respect, and trust. You expect obedience based on the knowledge of your love. God, our heavenly Father, who is much wiser then us asks and deserves this same love and trust-based obedience.

It is on this issue of faith all mankind is tested. It was on this very issue that Adam and Eve fell. They were given specific instructions not to eat the fruit of a specific tree [Gen.2:16,17]! The significance was that they failed to give love-based trust and obedience to God's commands ***even though they didn't fully understand***. The test of faith was given to Abraham to sacrifice Isaac and praise God he passed! It is the same principle with Sabbath observance of the fourth Commandment. The fundamental issue is: To whom will we give our obedience, worship, and allegiance? It is a test of faith.

For six thousand years the basis of the great controversy has been about allegiance and it is no surprise that it will be ***the issue*** at the closing of the conflict. Satan's goal was, and still is, to deface God's laws that instruct in allegiance and worship to God and to receive the worship only God deserves. Revelation tells us that in earth's closing moments three important messages of warning will be proclaimed to the world and all three involve the issue of worship [Rev.14:6-9].

When in the final days of earth's history you are being called to *"Fear God and give glory to him..."* How will you choose to show your allegiance? Will you follow His specific instructions to *"<u>Remember</u> the Sabbath day by keeping it holy..."* [Ex.20:8-11]. Will you claim the special blessing He offers: *"If thou* *turn away thy foot from the sabbath, from doing thy pleasure on my holy day; and call the sabbath a delight, the holy of the LORD, honourable; and shalt honour him, not doing thine own ways, nor finding thine own pleasure, nor speaking thine own words: Then shalt thou delight thyself in the LORD; and I will cause thee to ride upon the high places of the earth, and feed thee with the heritage of Jacob thy father: for the mouth of the LORD hath spoken it."* [Isa.58:13,14].

Giving worship to our Creator any time is a blessing; but, a richer and fuller spiritual blessing results from full obedience and submission to God's commands [Rev.22:14 KJV; Jn.15:10,11].

Appendix E
The Beast of Revelation

In the last days we are warned, *"If any man worship the beast and his image, and receive his mark in his forehead, or in his hand, The same shall drink of the wine of the wrath of God..."* Rev.14:9,10. Because it is God's desire for every person to be saved [2 Pet.3:9] He has given us eleven identifying characteristics of the "beast" in His Word to prevent being deceived.

Before we reveal who the "beast" is it is important to preface this information by saying that there are many God-loving, heaven-bound Christian friends affiliated with this religious institution who do not realize the they have been taught false doctrine. This is why, in mercy and love, God makes the plea "come out of her my people" [Rev.17:2-4].

According to Scripture a "beast" is a king or kingdom or ruler with great political power [Dan.7:17,23; 8:21]. Even today animals are symbols of nations–the United States being an eagle. The political power that has been clearly identified by Bible scholars from protestant denominations as the "beast" [Revelation 13:1; 14:9,10] is the Papacy or Roman Catholic Church. History reveals that this "diverse" ecclesiastical power controlled kingdoms and dominated the religious world for many centuries. Daniel described it as the "Little Horn" [Dan.7:8; 20-25; 8:9-12] and Paul referred to it as the "man of sin" [2Thes.2:2-4]. There is clearly no other power on earth that so precisely fits the following eleven Bible criteria. [Rev.13:1-10; 15-18].

(1) THE BEAST RISES OUT OF THE SEA (Rev.13:1) = In Scripture water such as "sea" represents a multitude of people, nations, and tongues [Rev.17:15]. So these beasts arose from an area of the densely populated civilized world. This describes perfectly the densely populated area of Rome in Western Europe where the Papal power arose and has its seat of power.

(2) THE BEAST HAS SEVEN HEADS AND TEN HORNS (Rev.13:1) = To positively identify the papacy as the seven headed and ten horned beast we can reference other Scriptures concerning the same subject matter. The beast described in Revelation 13 is actually an amalgamation of the forth beast described in Daniel's vision [Dan.7:15-20] and is also related to the toes of the statue in Nebuchadnezzar's dream [Dan.2:31-35].

It is well established in secular history and accepted by the Christian world that the beasts and parts of the statue in these prophecies represent the four major empires dominating the world [Dan.7:17,23] from 600 years before Christ to the final climax of earth's history. [*The Decline and Fall of the Roman Empire*, vol.3, p.634]. Review of these will establish who the seven heads and ten horns on the beast represent.

I. The Lion [Dan.7:4] or The Head of Gold [Dan.2:32] = Babylon's rule from 605 - 538 B.C. and was like a lion with eagle wings. A lion and head of gold perfectly described the empire of Babylon because it was the greatest of all kingdoms and the wings described the swiftness in which it conquered the civilized world.

II. The Bear [Dan.7:5] or The Breast and Arms of Silver [Dan.2:32] = Medo-Persia ruled from 538 - 331 B.C. The bear perfectly describes the cruel and rapacious characteristics of the Medes and Persians. The three ribs signify the three provinces of Babylon, Lydia, and Egypt. The bear being inferior to the lion and silver inferior to gold, describes how Medio-Persia was inferior to Babylon in wealth and magnificence.

III. The Leopard [Dan.7:6] or The Belly and Thighs of brass [Dan.2:32] = Greece ruled from 331 - 168 B.C. The four wings represent the conquests of Greece under Alexander that had no parallel in ancient times for rapidity in conquest of the then civilized world. The four heads represents the four generals to whom his kingdom was divided following his death.

IV. The Dreadful and Terrible Beast [Dan.7:7] or The Great Legs of Iron [Dan.2:33] = Rome and the ten horns ruled from 168 B.C. - 476 A.D. At its inception the empire of Rome was unequaled in the dread and terror it inspired as it ground nations into the dust beneath its feet.

The seven heads and ten horns [Rev.13:1] = Rome spilt into ten kingdoms between 351 A.D. - 476 A.D. Scripture also describes these as the ten horns of Daniel 7:7,20 and the ten toes on the statue of Daniel 2:4. The feet that were "iron mixed with miry clay" [Dan.2:43] represented these ten final divisions of the Roman empire. God said they "shall not cleave one to another" [Dan.2:43] and history proves with the futile efforts of Hitler in WW II that God's Word is true and these nations will never be reunited. These ten divisions were the Alamanni (Germans), Visigoths (Spanish), Franks (French), Suevi (Portugese), Burgundians (Swiss), Anglo-Saxons (English), Lombards (Italians) and the three who are now extinct the Ostrogoths, Vandals, and Heruli [Dan.7:24; Dan.2:4].

Then "another shall arise after them" [Dan.7:24; 7:8] also called the "Little Horn" [Dan.7:8], and a "diverse" kingdom [Dan.7:24] = While the first ten were political kingdoms this one was a diverse ecclesiastical power. This is the same power that rose up after the ten horns in Revelation 13:2. Out of the ruins of political Rome, arose the great Empire in the giant form of the Roman Church (A. C. Flick, *The Rise of the Mediaeval Church* [1900], p. 150). Her emergence began in the year of 476 and she rose to full power by 538 A.D. History and the Bible prove beyond a doubt that the "Little Horn"– [the dreaded beast of Rev.13:1; Dan.7:8; 7:24; Rev.14:9] is the Papacy.

She plucked up three horns by the roots [Dan.7:8; 7:20]. Proving her power, the Pope of Rome destroyed the Ostrogoths, Vandals, and Heruli because they refused to become "Christian" leaving seven heads.

(3) RECEIVES POWER, SEAT, AND AUTHORITY FROM THE DRAGON [Rev.13:2] = Satan is the "dragon" [Rev.20:2] giving the beast its power and political position. The "seat" of a kingdom is its capital. Herod, Rome's ruler, was clearly controlled by Satanic influence as he sought the death of Christ [Rev.12:3-5;12:9; 13:2; Matt.2:13]. It was this same pagan Rome, under the decree of Justinian, that fulfilled this prophecy by turning over her authority and capital city to the Papacy– "the dragon gave him his power, and his seat, and great authority."

(4) SEEKS WORSHIP AND IS GUILTY OF BLASHPHEMY [Rev.13:1,4,5,6,8; Dan.7:8,20] = The Bible describes blasphemy as an attack on the name of God [Rev.13:6]. In other words to claim to be God and claim the rights that only He has [Jn.10:32,33]. One specific privilege that only members of the Godhead can grant is forgiveness [Mk.2:9,10]. Here is a direct quote from a Catholic catechism: "The Priest does really and truly forgive the sins in virtue of the power given to him by Christ." Joseph Deharbe, S.J., A Complete Catechism of the Catholic Religion (New York: Schwartz, Kirwin & Fauss, 1924), p.279.

The Papal organization's leader has also claimed power over the angels of God. "Indeed, the excellence and power of the Roman pontiff is not only in the sphere of heavenly things, earthly things, and those of the lower regions, but even above the angels, than whom he himself is greater" (translated from Lucius Ferraris, Papa II, *Prompta Bibliotheca*, Vol. VI, p. 27

(5) THE BEAST WAS "LIKE" A LEOPARD, WITH FEET OF A BEAR, AND THE MOUTH OF A LION (Rev.13:2) = The "Leopard" headed by Alexander ordered his people to worship him as a god. The Papacy beast power of Revelation 13 ruled by the Pope took on the Greek culture of claiming worship as God.

The "bear" power, Medo-Persia, is still known today for its claims of infallibility. Once a law was made it could not be reversed [Dan.6:15]. The Pope "as the feet of a bear" claims this same infallibility.

The "Lion" empire Babylon, is still known today as a wonder of the world. Its prideful rulers blasphemously claim status and worship as God and so does the Pope–"his mouth as the mouth of a lion."

(6) RULES FOR 42 PROPHETIC MONTHS [Rev.13:5; 11:2; Dan.7:25] = The Bible says that the beast was given power to reign for 42 months. In prophecy one day equals one year [Ezek.4:6; Numb.14:34]. A Jewish month contained 30 days so 30 x 42 days equals 1260 years [Rev.11:3; 12:6]. The Little Horn or Papal powers ruled from 538 A.D. to 1798 exactly 1,260 years. This era was termed "The Dark Ages" because the church forbade all but the church leaders to read the Scriptures.

(7) PERSECUTED THE SAINTS [Rev.13:10; 17:6; Dan.7:25] = During the Papal rule those who did not submit to her dogmatic apostate beliefs were considered enemies of the church. Pressured by her power, the civil authorities under the direction of the "Inquisitional Courts," persecuted and killed Christians unwilling to recant their Bible-based beliefs. [New Catholic Encyclopedia - Washington, D.C.: The Catholic University of America, 1967, vol.14, p. 208: *Torture and the Church*].

(8) RECEIVES A DEADLY WOUND [Rev.13:3] = The Papal power temporarily ended when Rome was forced to retreat from the Arian invaders and the French general Berthier arrested and exiled Pope Pius VI– who died in prison. This deadly wound was delivered in 1798 right on the Biblical schedule.

(9) DEADLY WOUND HEALS AND "ALL THE WORLD WONDERED AFTER THE BEAST" [Rev.13:3] = The Scriptures also predicted that the deadly wound would heal. Since 1798 the Papal leaders have continued to regain influence and power. The leaders of all the countries of the world consider it a privilege to give honor to the Pope. As he travels the globe, the Pope is often the focus of television and newspaper headlines, gaining prestige as the world "wonders" after him.

(10) THE MAN HAS THE NUMBER 666 [Rev.13:18] = The man representing the Papal power is the Pope. The title he claims is, "Vicar of the Son of God." which is "Vicarious Filii Dei" in the official language of Latin. If you convert each letter of this title to Roman numerals–they total 666.

(11) HE WOULD ATTEMPT TO CHANGE "TIMES AND LAWS" [Dan.7:25] = The Beast power in its own publications blatantly claims authority over God to alter His laws. "The Pope has power to change times, to abrogate laws, and to dispense with all things, even the precepts of Christ." **Decretal, de Tranlatic Episcop**

The Catholic church has attempted to change God's ten commandments. The second commandment which forbids bowing down to images is removed, and the tenth which forbids coveting, is divided into two.

There is clearly no person or organization other than the Catholic Papacy that fits all these Bible-based criteria that God has provided in His Word to warn us who the beast power is.

Appendix F - The "Image" of the Beast

The "image" of the Beast must also be identified to avoid "the mark" [Rev.14:9]. Just as God provides information on how to identify the beast He has also provided 5 characteristics of its "image" so we can be fully informed and avoid receiving its mark.

There is only one nation that exists on earth today that meets the first three of these five predictions that have come to pass. The obvious is that the United States is on track to become the "image of the beast."

(1) CAME OUT OF THE EARTH [Rev.13:11] = Since we earlier discovered that Bible prophecy uses "water" to describe a heavily populated area [Rev.17:15] then we may conclude that the "earth" is a sparsely populated area. The United States did not conquer by force as the four beasts of Daniel 2 and 7 and Revelation 13 and 14. The United State rose to power in a sparsely populated land.

(2) WAS "COMING UP OUT OF THE EARTH" WHEN THE PAPACY RECEIVING ITS DEADLY WOUND [Rev.3:3,11] = We know from our study of the Beast that this deadly wound was delivered in 1798. On March 1, 1789 the Constitution of the United States went into effect. As predicted this newly emerging world power came into existence as the Papacy received her deadly wound.

(3) IT WAS "ANOTHER BEAST" [Rev.13:11] = According to John it was "another beast" so it could not be any other preexisting power. This criteria would rule out all the preexisting European countries as being the "image of the beast."

(4) HAD 2 HORNS AS A LAMB BUT SPAKE AS A DRAGON [Rev.13:11] = The lamb represents the gentleness offered in religious freedom to all. Then speaking as a "dragon" represents a later change in its original nature. The United States Constitution, based on the philosophy of freedom of worship, perfectly fits the description of the Lamb. The term "lamb" also indicates youthfulness–the United States came into existance after all the previously discussed beasts. The "two horns" on the lamb represents the United States' greatest claims of both civil and religious freedom.

(5) EXERCISES ALL THE POWER OF THE FIRST BEAST BEFORE IT TO FORCE WORSHIP [Rev.13:12;15]= In opposition to the forced participation in the "mother church" apostate teachings Martin Luther nailed the 95 Thesis on doctrinal error to the church door in Whittenburg marking the beginning of the great religious Reformation. The pursuing of this religious freedom was the motivating factor for those coming on the May Flower to establish this nation.

One hundred years ago it was common to hear this same information identifying the beast resounding from virtually all Protestant pulpits. This fact can be easily established by reading the sermons and historical notes about the founders of the different denominations. Now from the majority of them you don't hear this message. This is the wound of the Papacy continuing to heal. The theme of the day is to put away the past and join hands with the "mother church" that once forced her views on the people. Now Protestant churches, once a part of the Reformation, are readopting the beliefs of the "beast" power.

It doesn't take much effort to observe the terrible rise in crime over the last few decades. In fulfillment of Paul's prediction in the last days we are witnessing, "...fornication, wickedness, covetousness, maliciousness; full of envy, murder, debate, deceit, malignity; whisperers, Backbiters, haters of God, despiteful, proud, boasters, inventors of evil things, disobedient to parents, Without understanding, covenant breakers, without natural affection, implacable, unmerciful" [Rom.1:29-31]. The religious majority are tired of it and are ready to do something about it. They are organizing political parties and voting in leaders to use the church-state union to attempt to force their religious beliefs on others. They will "speak like a dragon" to change the very foundation of religious freedom that this great nation is based on–civil and religious freedom. All these efforts will be "to bring our nation back into God's favor."

In resemblance of the papal reign of terror this power will use civil government to inflict economic sanctions [Rev.13:15-17] and eventually the death penalty to those who refuse to participate in its religious dictates. This reuniting with the "mother church" in her apostate beliefs is what is referred to as the "image" of the beast [Rev.14:9].

Appendix G
God's "Seal" and the "Mark" of the Beast

The great controversy began and will end over the issue of worship–the demonstration of loyalty. The "mark" of the beast or the "seal" of God is a sign of who has our allegiance. Every living person will receive the "mark" of the beast by joining Satan in rebellion to God's law or receiving God's "seal" by choosing to obey all His commandments.

We are told that the "seal" or "mark" which indicates true or false worship, is located in the "forehead" or on the "hand" [Rev.14:9]. The "forehead" is the decision making portion of the brain and the "hand" represents action. These are not visible marks [Heb.10:16] but rather a choice followed by an action. God's sealed people "keep the commandments of God, and the faith of Jesus." [Rev.14:12]. The individuals who have received God's seal as commandment keepers will be protected through the seven plagues [Rev.9:4; 7:3]. Those who follow the apostate religious practices of the beast will receive its "mark" and suffer destruction [Rev.14:9-11].

You may ask, "Why is keeping God's commandments and specifically the fourth such an important issue?" We were warned by the prophet Daniel, in his vision that the beast power, motivated by Satanic influence, would "Think to change times and laws" [Dan.7:25]. The fourth commandment is the only one that involves time.

A "seal" contains three things: the ruler's name, title, and the domain under command. An earthly example is the presidential seal which contains the ruler's name, the title: "President" and the domain: "The United States of America." Located in the heart of God's law is the fourth commandment which contains every element of God's seal, "...the LORD [His name] made [title of Creator] heaven and earth, the sea [His domain]." Satan has focused his attack on the fourth commandment which calls us to remember and worship God as our Creator by keeping His day holy [Ex.20:8-11; Mk.2:28]. Satan has cleverly, over time, managed to blind the majority of the Christian world to the blessing and importance of the Sabbath. Just as God used Sabbath observance as a test of loyalty for the Children of Israel in the desert [Ex.16:4-6] it will be a testing point of our allegiance in the last days.

You may ask, "When is the mark of the beast received?" The Bible predicts the lamb-like beast will be transformed into the image of the beast and speak as a dragon [Rev.13:11]. Because of influence from the Papacy [the beast], the image of the beast [the Protestant churches reunited in the apostasy of false doctrine with the Papacy] will speak as a dragon by exerting pressure for all Christians to conform to the beast's religious practices. This will be done first by economic sanctions and eventually physical force. At that point every living person will have made the choice to accept God's "seal" by obeying His commandments [Rev.14:12; 12:17] despite persecution or receive the "mark" of the beast by observing its false doctrines [Rev.14:7-9]. Until the above events occur the mark of the beast will not be received by anyone. In mercy God is still calling His people out of the false doctrines of Babylon [Rev.18:1-4].

Certificate of Excellence

____

The Great Controversy Bible Study

This certificate is an official acknowledgment from a qualified instructor that the person named above has diligently and successfully completed The Great Controversy Bible Study Course.

______________	______	God	______________	______
Certified Course Graduate	Date	Witness	Certified Course Instructor	Date

Bible Study Guides

*** Prayer Groups!**
*** Prison Ministries!**
*** Personal Sharing!**
*** Church Study Groups!**
*** Classroom Workbook!**
*** Personal Devotion!**

Steps to Christ Bible Study Guide

This study guide, based on the classic soul winning book, "*Steps To Christ*", points the reader to Jesus Christ – the only One who is able to meet the needs of the soul. It unfolds the simplicity of Christ's saving grace and the victory offered to you by His keeping power. This life-changing book is now available in a Bible study format in Spanish or simplified English.

The Great Controversy Bible Study Guide

The commentary following the questions is the original text adapted from 13 of the last 14 abridged chapters of ***The Great Controversy.*** In a Bible study format, this life-changing publication presents the Biblical history of the great conflict between the powers of good and evil, between life and death. Starting from the origin of sin and concluding with its extermination, you will search out knowledge that will affect your eternal destiny. Just a few of the important topics covered are: communication with the dead; the law of God; observance of God's holy day; the mark of the beast; the time of trouble; the coming of Christ; and the destruction of the earth.

Seeds of Wisdom Christ's Object Lessons Bible Study Series

In teaching with parables, Christ's purpose was to use nature as a medium to teach the spiritual and connect us with the truths of His written Word. "*Seeds of Wisdom*" uses the parables based on seeds and plants from the classic, "*Christ's Object Lessons*" as commentary in a life-changing Bible interactive study series.

The Sanctified Life Bible Study Guide

Are you tired of playing spiritual games? Are you ready to experience the blessing that comes from full surrender and a daily connection with God? By studying the lives of Daniel, John, and the example of Christ, this guide will encourage, inspire, and challenge you to a deeper experience with God.

Promise of Peace Bible Study Guide

This study guide answers the following questions and many more. Who is God? What is His character like? Does God care for me as an individual? Is His Word trustworthy? How can I get to know and communicate with Him? How can I find freedom from guilt and have inner peace? What is temptation? Why do I struggle with sin? What is some practical, Bible based wisdom that brings victory and peace?